Photoelectric Astronomy
for Amateurs

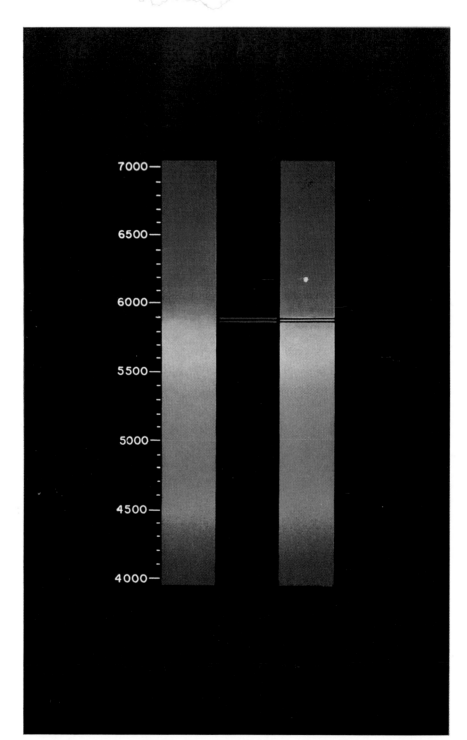

Photoelectric Astronomy

for Amateurs

Edited by

FRANK BRADSHAW WOOD

◀ The three principal types of spectra.
Left, a continuous spectrum.
Middle, an emission-line spectrum
(here, the strongest lines of the sodium atom).
Right, an absorption-line spectrum.

The Macmillan Company, New York

COLLIER-MACMILLAN LIMITED, LONDON

First Printing

Library of Congress catalog card number: 63-8638

THE MACMILLAN COMPANY, NEW YORK
COLLIER-MACMILLAN CANADA, LTD., TORONTO, ONTARIO

Printed in the United States of America

PREFACE

Probably no branch of science has received such impetus from the work of intelligent and enthusiastic amateurs as has the field of variable stars. Historically, stellar variability was first discovered by amateurs, and the number of variable star observers belonging to the various associations throughout the world must be numbered in the hundreds, if not in thousands. To date, most of the contributions have been based on visual estimates of the brightness of stars as seen through small telescopes. These observations have been of particular value in the field of long period variables, where the relatively large ranges have meant that high accuracy was not absolutely essential in tracing in a general way the changes of brightness with time.

Modern technology has now developed to the point where amateurs no longer need be dependent on visual measures alone. Indeed, a few amateurs have already built photoelectric equipment and have made useful observations with it. This book is written in an attempt to interest more observers in this sort of work and to indicate how suitable equipment can be built and used, what sort of objects will most profitably repay observations, and how such observations should be treated, once obtained.

Thirty years ago there were scarcely more than half a dozen observatories on this planet where systematic photoelectric photometry could be carried out. The photoelectric photometer of the thirties was a temperamental instrument and its use was limited to the brightest stars. Changes in technology have changed this, and now smaller telescopes can be used with photoelectric equipment to attack successfully problems in many branches of astronomy. It is hoped this book will point out some fields in which suitable work can be done and indicate how the attack can be made.

No effort has been made to avoid overlap between the chapters. This overlap may be useful because some readers may wish to read certain chapters and to omit others. A more basic reason is that it is felt that the readers may benefit by having topics of importance discussed from more than one point of view.

I sincerely hope that this book will be of value to amateur astronomers who wish to make the kind of serious and precise contributions made possible by modern photoelectric techniques.

FRANK BRADSHAW WOOD

CONTENTS

Photoelectric Astronomy
for Amateurs

CHAPTER 1

The Place of Photometry in Astronomy

HARLAN J. SMITH

Yale University Observatory

In human affairs we have long been accustomed to read important meanings from subtle appearances and changes. A person's blush at the mention of a name, a suspect's slight change of blood pressure at a question concerning a murder—such clues can suggest highly important implications to those with sufficient skill in observation and interpretation. For, to be sure, observation is not the whole story—an observation is normally meaningful only as part of a pattern, a model of the situation into which the observation can be fitted and through which it can be interpreted.

Stellar affairs show certain parallels with the examples mentioned. Thus in a sense some stars also blush. Likewise slight changes of their internal pressure can be detected by appropriate observations. Stars have been suspected of complicity in stellar cannibalism or even of contemplating suicide. As with the human case, stellar signs and changes are often subtle. In learning to read and interpret such clues, astronomers have found the precise study of brightness and its variations to be one of their most important tools.

Accordingly the rest of this book is devoted to the science of measuring intensity of light, its applications to astronomical light sources, and some of the implications of such measures. The emphasis of the book is on observational work which is within the reach of amateurs or professionals with modest equipment. But just as a map of a state is more meaningful if read in the context of its relation to the rest of the country, so an initial sketchy presentation of the place of photometry in astronomy may help clarify in turn the meaning and value of the photometry which any worker himself carries out. Much of the next two sections therefore concerns matters which this book is specifically not about. In particular we will take a brief, very general look at the principal kinds of direct astronomical observations, followed by a closer examination of the nature of light sources. The return to photometry begins with a history of the attempts to measure brightness and brings out reasons for some of the more curious customs still with the profession. The particular techniques and applications of modern photoelectric photometry and finally those most suitable for amateur or smaller scale professional work are briefly discussed.

Classical Astronomy

Any reader of this book is already generally aware of the magnificent architecture of the universe, of the solar system with its totally dominant single star orbited by a mixed debris of planets, asteroids, comets, dust particles, and gas, of the other similar and dissimilar stars and inter-stellar matter composing our vast Milky Way Galaxy, and of the hundreds of billions of other galaxies on out toward the fringes of the observable universe. It also has become common knowledge that individual elements of the universe are evolving, each star being born and passing through various interesting stages of development before fading away into an almost timeless white-dwarf senility. But partly because it is so obvious, we tend to forget that practically every element of this remarkable insight into the contents and span of space can be obtained only by careful observation of and shrewd deduction from just one basic type of clue—the light which reaches us in often barely detectable traces from the sky. Recently we have had to broaden our interpretation of the word "light," since radio wavelengths have now been added to the nominally optical regions of the observable spectrum, while rockets and satellites are beginning to make most of the remainder available as well. But historically, and for the forseeable future for amateurs, the traditional optical window through the atmosphere is the domain of astronomy.

In particular, with ordinary light the only things we can hope to observe *directly* are

1*a*. position on the sky from which the light appears to come
1*b*. change of this position with time
2*a*. brightness of the light at particular frequencies (colors) or over certain ranges of frequency
2*b*. change of such brightness with time.

Practically all of classical astronomy was devoted to 1*a* and *b* above. For more than 3,000 years astronomers measured with ever-increasing accuracy the appearances, positions, and motions of sun, moon, planets, and comets. Interpretation of the observations led to the remarkable structure of celestial mechanics and orbit theory—a subject still of much importance in theoretical astronomy and now of practical application to artificial satellites and space ships. Similarly, study of the positions of stars with respect to each other or according to well-defined celestial coordinate systems revealed the apparent annual motion (parallax) of some stars from which their distances follow, the mutual orbital motions of other stars from which knowledge of masses follows, and the steady drifts of still others which provide information about star clusters, about statistics of star distances, and about motions within the Milky Way galaxy. Such positional astronomy remains the foundation on which much of modern astronomy is based, and active work continues on the foundation.

The Nature of Light

From around 1800, and with growing momentum ever since, astronomers have not merely measured the direction on the sky from which light comes, but have closely studied its nature as well. Such work became possible because of the great discoveries in physics, mostly in the nineteenth century, concerning the sources and nature of light. In particular, experiments of John Herschel and others, Maxwell's theoretical work and the production of radio waves by Hertz finally made it clear that ordinary visible light is but one small part of the boundless electromagnetic spectrum (Fig. 1–1).

In its most intuitive sense, the spectrum is what one sees when with a prism he breaks up a beam of white light into its visible colors —plus all the invisible colors lying in and beyond the infrared and the ultraviolet. More rigorously, light proves to have a wave nature, in the sense that each spectral "color" whether visible or not can be identified with electromagnetic vibrations (waves) having a certain frequency (wavelength). Figure 1–1 also shows selected pairs of frequency and wavelength throughout the spectrum.

It is clear from the figure that frequency and wavelength are related but change in opposite senses. For electromagnetic waves in a vacuum —or, closely enough, in air—

$$\lambda \nu = c .$$

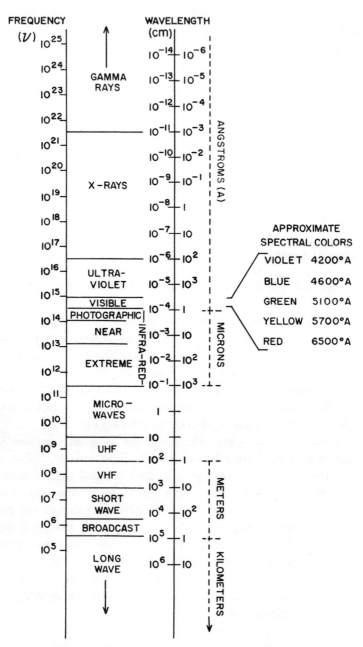

Fig. 1–1. The Spectrum of Electromagnetic Radiation.

That is, wavelength (λ) times frequency (ν) equals the velocity of light (c) which in the normally used metric system is almost exactly 3×10^{10} cm/sec or 3×10^8 m/sec. For example, the wavelength corresponding to a frequency of 10 M c/s is found as $\nu = 3 \times 10^8 \div 10 \times 10^6 = .3 \times 10^2 = 30$ m; or, as an example using ordinary light, the frequency corresponding to blue light of wavelength .00004 cm is $\nu = 3 \times 10^{10} \div 4 \times 10^{-5} = 0.75 \times 10^{15}$ cps. In general it is enough to specify either a frequency or a wavelength; the other is then determined, along with the spectral color.

For most physical measurements of length the centimeter is regarded as the basic unit, but appropriate multiples often are used in practice for convenience. Thus in the radio region the meter often is used for specifying the longer wavelengths, the centimeter for microwaves, and work is now beginning with millimeter waves. Still shorter waves fall into the infrared part of the spectrum where by long convention physicists have specified wavelengths in microns ($1\mu = .001$ mm $= 10^{-4}$ cm). Finally the still shorter waves including ordinary light, ultraviolet, x-rays and gamma rays are usually measured in *angstrom units* ($1\text{Å} = 10^{-8}$ cm), in commemoration of the Swedish physicist Ångström who not only employed the unit for the first time, thinking of it as a "tenth-meter" (10^{-10} m), but who also, around 1860–70, did the first really major work in determining accurate wavelengths of light. On this scale x-rays have wavelengths typically of a few angstroms, a sunburn is generated largely by ultraviolet radiation in the range 3,000–4,000Å, human eyes are able to respond to light ranging from violet (4,000Å) to deep red (7,000Å), and the extreme infrared limit to which photographic plates have been successfully sensitized and used is about 13,000Å. Figure 1–1 also gives approximate wavelengths for the central regions of each major visible spectral color.

Wavelength can be measured to very high accuracy (of the order of $\pm.0001\text{Å}$) with the aid of large spectrographs, which in principle are nothing but enormous dispersing prisms with precise means of measuring where each wavelength falls. In practice, spectrographs normally employ diffraction gratings instead of prisms to disperse the light into its colors, and use additional lenses or mirrors to image the light as required (Fig. 1–2).

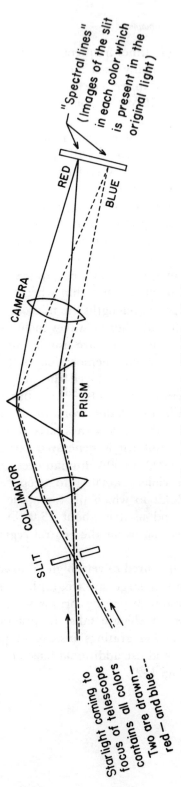

SLIT COLLIMATOR CAMERA RED BLUE

PRISM

"Spectral lines"
(Images of the slit
in each color which
is present in the
original light)

Starlight coming to
focus of telescope
contains all colors—
Two are drawn—
red — and blue---

Fig. 1–2. The Principle of the Spectrograph.

Light Sources and their Associated Radiation

With such a variety of light sources in the universe, one might expect to find a hopelessly bewildering variety of kinds of spectra. Actually, as was first emphasized by Kirchhoff around 1860, spectra fall very naturally into only two general classes which we now call *continuous* and *line* respectively. The meanings are almost self-evident: a continuous spectrum has light more or less uniformly present throughout its length; a line spectrum has light either present or absent at discrete, relatively sharp positions—wavelengths—in the spectrum. Examples are shown in the frontispiece.

Continuous spectra. A continuous spectrum is produced by any hot glowing solid or liquid or by hot gas under sufficiently high pressure —examples of these being respectively a lightbulb filament, a puddle of molten iron, and the light streaming out from the interior of a star. This form of light emission is familiar from the universal experience of putting a metal object in a fire and watching it grow more luminous as its temperature rises. Because such radiation depends essentially on the *temperature* rather than the particular emitting substance, it is called *thermal* radiation.

Experimentally the *amount* of thermal radiation was found to increase with the fourth power of the temperature (Stefan-Boltzmann relation), while the average color of the light becomes more blue as the temperature rises (Wien's relation). These relations are essential for understanding the applications of photometry to astronomy.

To provide a satisfactory theoretical explanation of thermal radiation, Planck, around 1900, was forced to introduce the quantum hypothesis, namely that energy instead of being infinitely divisible comes in smallest pieces, or *quanta*. As Einstein then pointed out, this suggests that radiation, although certainly wavelike in many ways, also has a *particle* aspect. Specifically, for any given wavelength there is a smallest possible packet of energy having that wavelength; such packets are now called *photons*, and can be thought of as the individual particles making up a beam of light. The shorter the wavelength (bluer) the photon, the more energy it carries.

These concepts concerning continuous thermal—sometimes called "Planck" or "black-body"—radiation have immediate immensely important applications in astronomy and photometry. As one specific

example, the total amout of light which a star can radiate depends
on the product of only two things: how much light it pumps out from
each unit area of surface, and how many such unit areas make up the
entire surface. The first of these factors is specified by the temperature
through Planck's Law, while the second—the total area of the star—
follows at once from the radius (area $= 4\pi R^2$). That is, if we can
find the effective *temperature* and the *size* of a star, we also know how
much light it must be radiating (its absolute magnitude). Much of
the importance of photometry stems from the fact that both of the
necessary quantities—temperature and size—can be studied by
photometry. Specifically, since there is a nearly perfect correlation
between temperature and star color, we only need to measure photometrically a star's color in order to estimate its temperature. Further,
as brought out in detail in the chapter by J. E. Merrill, important
information about the sizes of stars comes from photometric study
of eclipsing stars.

For many years thermal radiation was the only genuinely continuous radiation known. Two other mechanisms producing an effectively continuous spectrum were discovered recently. *Synchrotron*
radiation arises when electrons moving at a significant fraction of
the velocity of light travel in a region having a magnetic field. The
field forces the electrons to move in spiral paths. The resultant continuous change of direction is felt by each electron as a continuous
acceleration, and it has long been known that accelerated electrons
give off electromagnetic waves. If the amount of material and its
velocities are great enough and the field strong enough, a substantial
amount of visible light may be emitted by this process. Much of the
light of several celestial sources, the best known being the famous
Crab Nebula in Taurus, apparently is synchrotron in origin. The
other novel source, whose astronomical applications are tenuous as
yet, is *Cerenkov* radiation, arising as a sort of bow wave whenever a
particle moves through a medium faster than the velocity of light
for that medium (this being possible since the velocity of light in many
nonvacuum situations becomes greatly retarded). However, having
paid brief respects to the newcomers, we should remember that in
practically all astronomical situations ordinary thermal radiation is
the mechanism of the powerful sources of continuous radiation.

Line spectra.   In distinction to continuous radiation, line spectra arise from relatively uncompressed gasses. Specifically, if the atoms of a gas are excited in some way such as by heat or by electric discharge through them, they will emit only specific wavelengths of light, with no emission whatever at wavelengths between the permitted ones. Light normally enters a spectrograph through a fine slit; the successive images of this slit in all the various colors side by side make the spectrum. When the light source is a hot gas, the only images formed are those for which wavelengths are present in the incoming beam of light—that is, the resulting spectrum consists of a pattern of separated sharp lines of colors successively grading through the spectrum. The precise pattern of lines proves to depend primarily on the chemical elements and molecules present in the gas, also to some degree on the temperature and pressure of the gas. The lines are typically a fraction of an angstrom wide in stellar spectra, but some of the strongest lines show wings extending 10 or 15 angstroms to either side of the center.

In stellar spectra the lines arising from a given element are usually seen not in emission but as the identical pattern of wavelengths subtracted out of a continuous spectrum, that is, as an *absorption spectrum* (see the frontispiece). This effect arises because a gas is capable of absorbing the same wavelengths it can emit; hence if we look through a gas at a hotter continuous source, the gas will pass freely all radiations it cannot absorb, and in these wavelengths we will see the continuous spectrum undimmed. But for each wavelength where absorption is possible, the gas will absorb some of the radiation coming from the background, reradiating much of it back toward the source or off to the side, or converting it into other wavelengths. In either event the background continuous spectrum becomes dimmed in just these spectral lines which are characteristic of the gas. Something very much like this happens in the atmosphere of each star, where the flood of light from the hot, high-pressure interior constitutes a continuous spectrum emerging from the star; a somewhat cooler atmosphere acts in effect to screen out some of the energy in those wavelengths characteristic of the chemical elements and molecules present in the atmosphere.

Whether absorption or emission lines are present in a given star, their presence provides the astrophysicist with a wealth of detailed information on such matters as chemical composition, pressure, temperature, and distribution of matter in depth. Precise measures of their wavelengths also reveal small displacements from the laboratory positions, corresponding to Doppler shifts arising from relative motion toward or away from the observer. That is, the spectral lines provide an almost direct-reading speedometer for motions in the line of sight, giving astronomers precise information about motions of sun and stars in the galaxy, orbital motion of stellar pairs and systems, rotational motions of individual stars, and even turbulent motions in stellar atmospheres. A large proportion of astrophysics has to do with the observation and interpretation of spectral lines.

Nature of Photometry

Returning now to the original listing of possible things to do with light, we see that classical astronomy, despite its great achievements, by concentrating exclusively on the direction to light sources made only very slight use of the information carried by light. Observations of brightness, in particular at each wavelength with the light spread out into a spectrum, are necessary to make the picture more complete. Ideally one should measure accurately the intensity of light at each wavelength interval which can be resolved in the spectrum. This elaborate procedure, known as spectrophotometry, has a great future with photoelectric techniques, but compared to other methods of study it is so complicated and time consuming that relatively little spectrophotometry has been done despite its importance. Also, dispersing light into a spectrum is wasteful in the sense that the light, collected by a telescope, which originally could be concentrated in a single tiny star image, must now be spread out over anywhere from hundreds to millions of times the area of the single star image, reducing the brightness at each point accordingly and making it difficult or impossible to work with faint stars.

Fortunately for the rapid progress of astronomy, over the last century the realization has grown that an extraordinary amount of information comes from use of a far simpler technique—the measurement of the "total" brightness of stars and other objects. This is the ordinary use of the word *photometry* in astronomy. Of course it is not really possible to measure the total light since atmosphere, instrument, and light-detector impose limits on the spectral region observed. But this feature, once believed to be a drawback, now is recognized as one of the most valuable aspects of photometry.

In practice, then, astronomical photometry normally refers to

1. comparison of the brightness of different stars in the same broad spectral band,
2. measurement of different broad-band spectral regions in the light of a particular star, and
3. following of variations of brightness of a single star.

The remainder of this chapter and of the book is about these techniques and applications. But before taking them up in detail, some historical background may be useful in order to indicate why and how present techniques took the form they now have.

THE DEVELOPMENT OF PHOTOMETRY

The Magnitude System

The first astronomer to concern himself seriously with star brightnesses appears to have been Hipparchus, generally agreed to be the greatest astronomer of antiquity, who made major contributions to nearly every branch of classical astronomy. Around 120 B.C., in the first extensive catalogue of naked-eye stars, Hipparchus apparently graded the stars according to their brightness into six groups, or magnitudes. The brightest were called *alpha*, or first, magnitude; those which seemed to be on the average about half as bright were listed as *beta* or second magnitude, and so on down to the sixth magnitude, the faintest stars visible to the naked eye.

This original catalogue of Hipparchus no longer survives. But three centuries later it was copied by Claudius Ptolemy in an astronomical masterpiece which survived the Dark Ages through adoption by the star-loving Arabs who thought of it as the greatest (*al megiste*) work on astronomy. Reintroduced into Europe around the thirteenth century, it acquired its present name of *Almagest*. The astronomy and star catalogue in the Almagest were not firmly superseded until the seventeenth century; even then new star charts and catalogues were often based on the Almagest.

Thus, for very nearly 2,000 years Hipparchus' star tables—and magnitudes—were the basis of stellar astronomy. It is little wonder that the magnitude system, quaint as it now seems to those encountering it for the first time, caught on and has remained firmly fixed in astronomy—especially since the now-recognized logarithmic character of the magnitude scale actually offers certain advantages in computations over what at first seems more natural, namely using a simple linear intensity scale.

Astronomers generally used the magnitude scale as transmitted by Ptolemy relatively uncritically, or modified it to their own convenience as in the pioneering work of the great telescope maker and stellar astronomer, William Herschel, who shortly before 1800 made careful intercomparisons of many stars to determine their relative brightness and who extended his scheme to telescopic magnitudes.

The magnitude scale was finally put on its modern basis through a suggestion made by Pogson in 1856. The magnitudes of Hipparchus were related to actual stellar brightness—intensity—in such a way that each magnitude step was two to three times fainter than the previous one. To retain this pattern while nevertheless making it homogeneous and suitable for computation, Pogson defined a system such that each magnitude interval corresponds to a factor of exactly $\sqrt[5]{100}$, or 2.512, in intensity.

Under the leadership of Pickering at Harvard, the astronomical world soon adopted and has since retained this well-defined scheme. Magnitudes must now fit the *Pogson scale*, identical with that described above. Analytically, this means that the ratio of intensity of two stars must correspond to their difference of magnitude as follows:

$$I_1/I_2 = (\sqrt[5]{100})^{(m_2 - m_1)} = (2.512)^{(m_2 - m_1)}$$

By taking common logarithms of both sides, this can also be written as

$$\log(I_1/I_2) = 0.4(m_2 - m_1) ,$$

or as

$$m_2 - m_1 = 2.5 \log(I_1/I_2) .$$

Table 1–1 summarizes the magnitude-intensity relation over the range of common interest.

Table I-I

Relation between Magnitude Difference and Intensity Ratio. (Magnitude differences are given in the columns headed $m_2 - m_1$, with their corresponding intensity ratios I_1/I_2)

$m_2 - m_1$	I_1/I_2	$m_2 - m_1$	I_1/I_2	$m_2 - m_1$	I_1/I_2	$m_2 - m_1$	I_1/I_2	$m_2 - m_1$	I_1/I_2	$m_2 - m_1$	I_1/I_2
0.000	1.000	.01	1.009	.1	1.096	1	2.512	6	251.2	11	25,120
.001	1.001	.02	1.019	.2	1.202	2	6.310	7	631.0	12	63,100
.002	1.002	.03	1.028	.3	1.318	3	15.85	8	1585	13	158,500
.003	1.003	.04	1.038	.4	1.445	4	39.81	9	3981	14	398,100
.004	1.004	.05	1.047	.5	1.585	5	100.00	10	10,000	15	1,000,000
.005	1.005	.06	1.057	.6	1.738						etc.
.006	1.006	.07	1.067	.7	1.905						
.007	1.006	.08	1.076	.8	2.089						
.008	1.007	.09	1.086	.9	2.291						
.009	1.008										

One can find intermediate values which are not explicitly tabulated simply by multiplying the intensities which correspond to the digits of the magnitude difference, as in the following example. The apparent visual magnitude of Vega is 0.04, of Deneb 1.26. The difference is

$$1.22 = 1.00 + .20 + .02 \text{ mag} .$$

Correspondingly, Vega is

$$2.512 \times 1.202 \times 1.019 = 3.08$$

times brighter than Deneb.

Notice that any difference of five magnitudes always corresponds to a ratio or factor of 100 in intensity; ten magnitudes, to 100^2 or 10,000 in intensity, etc.

The behavior of the magnitude system for small magnitude differences is also noteworthy. Up to about 0.2 magnitude there is very little error in thinking of the magnitude difference as numerically equal to the intensity ratio in per cent. Thus, for instance, 0.03 magnitude difference between two stars means that the two stars have approximately the intensity ratio 1.03; that is, they differ in intensity by about 3 per cent. As another example of such usage, if one measures the brightness of a star with an error of 1 per cent he knows its magnitude with an uncertainty of about ± 0.01 magnitude.

While it is of course possible to carry on all astronomical measures and computations in ordinary intensity units—indeed interim computations are often done this way in practice—from now on we will follow the nearly universal custom in astronomy of expressing all basic arguments and results in magnitudes.

Techniques of Measurement

To measure light one must somehow catch and register it. So far only three basic types of light receptors have been widely used in astronomy—visual, photographic, and photoelectric. Since each has current as well as historic importance, it is worth while to compare their techniques and results.

Visual photometry. We have to exert some imagination to appreciate the problems facing scientists of several centuries ago who first became aware of the need to make really accurate comparisons of brightness.

Only the eye was available to serve as a detector, and the eye is notoriously unable to evaluate intensity intervals. Even with a great deal of practice, no one can look at isolated lights—for example, stars—and state their intensity ratio or magnitude difference accurately.

Today, when faced with a difficult measuring problem involving badly calibrated or seriously nonlinear detectors, scientists often fall back on null methods—the reduction in a measured way of the quantity being studied until it equals a definite standard, or vice versa. This approach is advantageous because the point of equality can be determined precisely even with grossly nonlinear detectors, while the measured attenuation permits computing back to the original value being sought.

Actually this principle of null-measurement is very old. In the present context, Huyghens, following a suggestion by Gregory, employed it around 1690 for one of the earliest astronomically important photometric observations—namely the first rough measure of the distance of a star. In effect his experiment assumed that Sirius and the sun had the same intrinsic brightness. Then, since the apparent brightness of a light declines with the square of its distance, the distance of Sirius could be determined in multiples of the sun's distance simply by measuring how many times fainter than the sun Sirius appeared to be. This measurement in turn was accomplished by use of a succession of pinholes designed to reduce the apparent size (actually brightness) of the sun to that of Sirius.

Huyghen's value for the distance of Sirius was too small by a factor of 20, partly because of errors in the photometry but also because Sirius, instead of being intrinsically equal to the sun in brightness, is actually 23 times brighter. Huyghen's remarkable experiment serves not only to point up the need for accuracy in photometry, but also to bring out a basic principle for finding astronomical distances which is, with appropriate inclusion of intrinsic brightness, the most prevalent one in use today.

Other and better null-comparison systems were devised in the latter half of the nineteenth century to make possible the apparent reduction of one star's brightness to equality with another or with a standard light source. The most important of these was the Zöllner photometer, in which the telescopic image of a real star could be compared with the image of an artifical star whose apparent brightness could be varied in a precisely determined way by rotating polarizing prisms. Variations of this instrument were used to form the great *Revised Harvard Photometry* and Potsdam *Durchmusterung* catalogues containing over 40,000 stars with magnitudes generally accurate to better than 0.10 mag. Published shortly after 1900, these catalogues mark the high tide of the visual era in photometry.

Magnitudes determined by the human eye are, not surprisingly, called *visual magnitudes*. It is necessary to be explicit about this because the dark-adapted eye, in responding really strongly only to a relatively narrow band of wavelengths lying roughly between 4,500 and 5,700Å, compares the brightness of stars effectively in this spectral range, an important point when we come to consider differences between stars.

Today visual photometry has one principal remaining use—the rapid estimate of magnitudes of variable stars. Interposition of the brightness of a variable among those of several adjoining comparison stars of different but known magnitude can be done in a few seconds with no more equipment than the eye, usually aided with binoculars for brighter stars or a telescope for fainter ones. A good observer can reliably interpolate a variable between comparisons of known brightness to better than ±0.2 mag. For some problems such as monitoring of long-period variables, timing minima of eclipsing binaries, checking flare stars or repeating novae, such precision is adequate and well justified by the speed and economy.

The continued usefulness of such work today is suggested by the number of variable stars still observed visually by the widespread fellowship of the American Association of Variable Star Observers and by equivalent organizations elsewhere in the world. About 60,000 individual observations are reported each year to the AAVSO, while their record on certain peculiar and interesting stars is essentially unbroken for more than forty years.

Despite its several positive factors visual photometry has grave handicaps. Perhaps the worst is the difficulty of setting up a true Pogson scale over a wide range of magnitudes. Almost equally serious are the typical errors of about ±0.2 mag. per observation (although these could be greatly reduced by the use of Zöllner or other photometers). From the theory of errors, 400 such observations would be required to bring the error of the average down to ±0.01 mag., a precision required for some modern investigations. If there are systematic as well as random errors in the visual work, as will almost invariably be the case, no number of observations will reduce the error below the level of the systematic effects. One major example of such systematic errors is the marked difference in color sensitivity of different observers' eyes.

Anyone doing photometry of any kind should nevertheless make at least a few attempts to estimate visually the brightness of several variables or of known constant stars in a standard sequence. This is one of the best ways to achieve some respect for the work of the past, to develop a real feeling for the meaning of a magnitude, and to appreciate properly the newer methods.

Photographic photometry. Soon after the invention of photography, its application to the heavens was pioneered at the Harvard Observatory under Bond and others, beginning in 1850. In the first flush of enthusiasm over the new methods, Bond wrote "The intensity and size of the images, taken in connection with the length of the time during which the plate has been exposed, measures the relative magnitudes of the stars." While this proved to be roughly true, increasingly careful work over the next half-century showed that photographic photometry also has certain almost insuperable problems. It may seem simple to photograph stars and to measure the size or the amount of blackening of each star image on the photographic plate, relating this somehow to magnitudes; however in practice such methods yield results only a little better than the best visual work.

The basic trouble with photographic magnitudes arises from the way an emulsion responds to light, in particular the behavior summarized in the *characteristic curve* for the particular emulsion. Figure 1–3 is a typical characteristic curve, showing first that there is a pre-exposure background level which will appear much the same however much light falls on it, up to a certain point. Still greater amounts of light put the emulsion beyond the threshold and then into the linear part of the characteristic curve, where over a certain range of light exposure the darkening response of the emulsion is directly proportional to the number of photons reaching the emulsion. Next comes a shoulder and finally a saturation region in which no amount of further exposure will significantly increase the amount of darkening; in fact the emulsion may even begin to reverse when exposures beyond ordinary saturation are used.

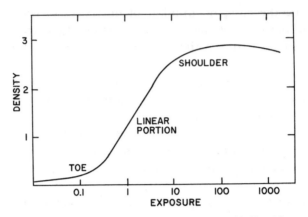

Fig. 1–3. The Characteristic Curve of a Photographic Emulsion.

If all of astronomical work could be confined to the linear part of the characteristic curve of some emulsion, there would be no serious problem of photometry. Actually, however, a star image formed by a telescope is a complicated thing. With a perfect refractor the image will be nearly circular, but will have a steep gradient of intensity from the center outwards with some of the light falling really quite far from the center. With a reflector this basically circular image has further troubles, including diffraction patterns from the secondary-mirror supports plus comatic flare for images which are even slightly off axis. Each part of the image is thus being formed at a different part of the characteristic curve of the emulsion. If all stars were of the same brightness, this would be of little concern; but since it is precisely the measurement of different brightness that is being attempted, the integrated blackening of star images bears only an extremely complicated relation to the relative magnitudes of the stars. Even worse, the relation between the response of the emulsion for different stars varies from one exposure to the next on the same star field because of differences in effective exposure time, quality of seeing and guiding, and development. For these and other reasons, photographic photometry can normally be done only on a strictly relative basis, by interpolating star images between those of standard stars of known magnitude on the same plate. Clearly, photographic methods are inherently comparative rather than fundamental in nature.

However, deliberate defocusing or spreading of star images over significant areas of carefully calibrated plates makes possible semi-absolute Pogson scaling over limited ranges of brightness. Employing such laborious techniques in as many different ways as could be devised, some magnificent photographic work was carried out in the early twentieth century. The best example, done at the Harvard and Mt. Wilson observatories, was the North Polar Sequence wherein the magnitudes of over 100 stars ranging down to twentieth magnitude were established as the definitive standards for photometry all over the sky. The success of such work depended heavily on earlier outstanding studies by K. Schwarzschild which established the theoretical basis of photographic photometry.

Through the first three decades of the present century many other lists of photographic magnitudes appeared, especially the great Selected Area Catalogues of Mt. Wilson, giving photographic magnitudes supposedly good to about ± 0.1 mag. for sequences in each of 139 Kapteyn Selected Areas, down to about nineteenth magnitude. Actually, however, a grave departure from a true Pogson scale had occurred in the faintest magnitudes.

Photographic photometry remains extremely valuable and widely used today. With a well-calibrated photoelectric sequence of stars available on the plate, and the use of an iris-diaphragm (Siendentopf or Eichner) type of photometer to measure what is effectively the diameter of star images on the plate, accuracies approaching ± 0.02 mag. can be achieved over substantial magnitude ranges.

When we remember that a single photographic plate can record up to millions of star images, and that even very close ones can be resolved on a good plate, it is clear that enormous telescope economy can be achieved by photographing a region and analyzing the star brightnesses later at leisure. Photographs also permit one to search for variables on a mass-production basis—the individual checking of stars one by one being forbiddingly slow except for very special purposes. These and other applications insure that the photographic emulsion is not likely to be replaced very soon as the ultimate repository for stellar records, although more advanced techniques such as digitized tape recorder records of scans of photosensitive tube faces may ultimately become competitive for some purposes.

Color index.   Astronomers working with photography soon discovered that most stars show different relative magnitudes when measured photographically than when observed visually. The reason is clear from the nature and behavior of the complex spectrum of a star, coupled with the different spectral response of the eye and the photographic film. To a reasonable approximation most stars show a Planck spectrum corresponding to a definite temperature (e.g., the curve lower in Fig. 1–4). Higher temperature not only raises the entire curve, but distributes the energy preferentially into the shorter, bluer wavelengths (curve 2). As already noted, the eye responds most strongly to wavelengths around 5,500Å, and has fallen off radically in sensitivity by about 4,300 and 6,500Å. On the other hand the photographic plate, unless specifically treated, responds only to wavelengths shorter than about 4,500Å. Since the older refractors used in the early days of photographic photometry normally had a flint-glass component opaque to ultraviolet light much below 3,900Å, the photographic wavelengths occupied a narrow band centered around 4,200Å. Idealizing both response bands to sharp edges, we see that visual and photographic measures of the same star were not measuring the same light at all. Such magnitudes would bear a constant relation to each other from star to star only if all stars had the same shape of Planck curves (which

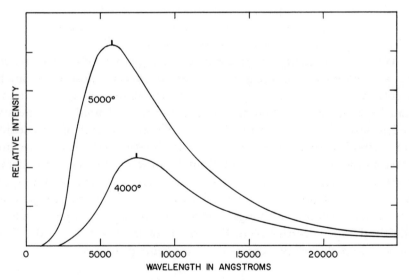

Fig. 1–4. Stellar Radiation as a Function of Wavelength.

of course is not true since stars differ very widely in temperature) and if there were no absorption effects in the stellar atmospheres.

To see this better, imagine two stars, A very hot and B quite cool, whose respective Planck curves are shown side by side in Figure 1–5. Photographic and visual sensitivity bands are indicated. Though the two stars have about the same visual magnitude, the hotter star is clearly much brighter in photographic magnitude. Since this extra brightness lies on the blue side of the spectrum, the integrated color of star A is distinctly bluer than that of star B. In general, the hotter the star the bluer its color, and conversely, the cooler the star the redder its color.

A very satisfactory way to handle such difficulties is precisely to take advantage of them by obtaining for each star a new quantity, the *color index*, defined as the difference between the apparent photographic magnitude (m_{pg}) and the apparent visual magnitude (m_v). Thus:

$$C. I. = m_{pg} - m_v \ .$$

In the example given in Figure 1–5, the color index will, of course, be different numerically for the two stars. But notice that since greater brightness means *smaller* numerical magnitude the bluer star will have the smaller color index number.

Really accurate color indices first became attainable when panchromatic films, sensitive to longer wavelengths than 4,500Å, were produced. Use of such films plus appropriate color filters makes possible apparent photovisual magnitudes (m_{pv}) closely comparable to, but more reliable than, the old visual magnitudes.

Color index has become one of the most important items of information we can know about a star, partly because it can be determined quickly, easily, and precisely for any star (there are all too few quantities pertaining to the stars for which this can be said), and more specifically because it is normally a good measure of the general range in which the surface temperature of a star must lie.

With more distant stars selective absorption of blue light by the interstellar medium can change the apparent color, making the stars seem too red. But when independent information concerning surface temperature is available through precise spectral classification, the observed color index then is able to indicate the amount of interstellar absorbing material between the star and the observer.

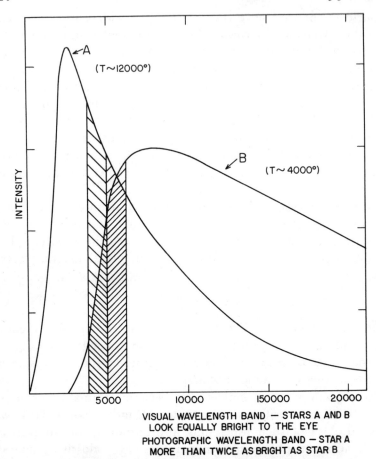

VISUAL WAVELENGTH BAND — STARS A AND B
LOOK EQUALLY BRIGHT TO THE EYE
PHOTOGRAPHIC WAVELENGTH BAND — STAR A
MORE THAN TWICE AS BRIGHT AS STAR B

Fig. 1–5. Photographic- and Visual-Magnitude Sensitivity
Regions on Planck Curves Corresponding to Stars of
Different Temperature (color).

Photoelectric photometry. Now that we have some slight appreciation
of the difficulties of doing really accurate visual or photographic
photometry, it is easy to see why astronomers might well have flocked
to photoelectric methods as soon as they became available shortly
after 1900. For the photoelectric effect over an enormous range of
brightness is *linear*. A certain amount of light (number of photons per
second) releases a certain number of electrons; *n* times as much light
releases precisely *n* times as many electrons. The problem of comparing star brightnesses is thus reduced to the problem of measuring

and comparing electric currents—a relatively easy thing to do accurately.

Actually, with several brilliant exceptions, astronomers in general were astonishingly slow to pick up the new technique. (This can perhaps be compared with the rather similar lag which occurred after Jansky's discovery of radio waves from space in 1933; it was nearly twenty years before a significant number of professional astronomers began to take a real interest in radio astronomy. Indeed an inspired and dedicated radio amateur and engineer, Grote Reber, for a decade developed radio astronomy single-handedly.) In photometry the first serious photoelectric work was by young professional astronomers—in particular Stebbins in the United States and Guthnik in Germany, who carved out their field in rather lonely grandeur for several decades.

Most of the earliest work was done using delicate, homemade selenium photoconductive cells, whose low sensitivity permitted work only on the very brightest stars. After 1911 potassium hydride photoelectric cells proved to be a great advance. Recording was normally done by directly reading an extremely sensitive galvanometer. Improvements in cells and techniques, and their use with larger telescopes, gradually expanded the applicability of photoelectric methods. By 1930, using a 15-inch telescope it was possible to work with seventh magnitude stars.

An important advance was Whitford's adaption in 1932 of electronic amplifiers to step up the feeble photocurrents to the place where ordinary meters or even pen recorders could be used.

In the subsequent thirty years more sensitive photocells and the principle of internal electron multiplication discussed below have made it possible to work photoelectrically on stars fainter than can be photographed with a given telescope.

In principle there is now only one factor limiting the precision of magnitude measures obtainable photoelectrically—namely the statistics of production of photoelectrons by the light from a given star with a given telescope and photometer at a given time. Accuracies of better than a ten-thousandth of a magnitude should theoretically be easily attainable for brighter stars. But in practice the atmosphere sets severe limits of several kinds which restrict routine photoelectric photometry to precisions of about ± 0.01 magnitude for short single readings. These atmospheric effects include irregularities of transparency, imperfectly known (even if regular) transparency, "seeing," wandering of the star image, and scintillation effects. Also, even if the atmosphere were no hazard, small differences in effective color sensitivity between individual photoelectric systems would render the resulting magnitudes imperfectly comparable at about the 0.01 mag. level for some kinds of stars. However, consistency approaching ± 0.002 mag. within a particular photometric system has been obtained meaningfully for some types of observations such as the average light curve of an eclipsing binary star.

MODERN PHOTOELECTRIC PHOTOMETRY

We are now ready to consider in more detail what constitutes a complete photoelectric photometer.

Telescope and diaphragm. The first element of an astronomical photo-electric photometer is really the telescope to which it is attached, whose two overlapping functions are to produce images of particular celestial objects in the focal plane where they can be isolated and studied individually, and to concentrate into each specific separate image all the light from that object which originally entered the tube.

At the focal plane is normally placed an opaque plate having a tiny hole—the diaphragm. When the telescope is properly aimed, only the light from a particular desired star or spot on the sky can pass through the diaphragm to the photocell beyond. In order not to cut out any of the star's light or to make its centering in the hole too critical, the diaphragm cannot be too small. Yet the larger it becomes the more light from the sky around the star also comes through and the more chance there is of including other unwanted stars in the measurement. Such stars may be five or six magnitudes fainter and quite invisible to the eye, yet they contribute an appreciable error in precise work. Accordingly, and particularly when working with fainter stars, the diaphragms are kept as small as one can get away with (even down to five seconds of arc), subject to seeing conditions, the stability of the telescope mounting, and the imaging quality of the telescope.

Refractors, though often used, are poor for photometry because they cut out ultraviolet light and because of their inability to bring light of all colors to a common focus. This is very serious because a crisp image in one color is always surrounded by a halo of poorly focused light of other colors, requiring the diaphragm to be painfully large (sometimes as much as a minute of arc) in order to accept most of the light passed by the filters. On the other hand, well-made and well-mounted reflectors make good economical light-buckets for photometry over an almost indefinitely wide spectral range.

Fabry lens. Directly behind the diaphragm is normally placed a Fabry lens, whose function is simply to form an image of the illuminated objective of the telescope on the photocell. It can be thought of as a sort of light homogenizer, smoothing out the star image into a uniform (apart from scintillation effects) small disk of illumination on the photocell, and making the entire system relatively independent of small irregularities in guiding on the star. Without the Fabry lens small excursions of the star image, even thought it remained within the diaphragm, would shift the illumination of a small sharp star image onto different parts of the photocell. Since the photosensitive surface is never truly uniform, such excursions could lead to serious spurious variations in the apparent brightness of the star.

Color system. Either before or after the diaphragm provision is normally made to insert colored filters, usually of glass because of their stability. These, coupled with the intrinsic sensitivity of the photocell and the transmissivity of the telescope, determine the wavelength region being recorded. Appropriate combinations exist to match closely the old visual and photographic ranges of sensitivity, as well as many other color ranges not normally employed in earlier work. In particular, much photometry has been done with the P, V system which was chosen because of its close match with the old pg, pv. More recently the three-color Johnson U, B, V (ultraviolet, blue, visual) system has proved advantageous in many kinds of work, although there are problems in which an R (red) or even an I (infrared) range has advantages over U as a third color.

Such filter systems can of course be proliferated; for example some of the most important photometry ever published has been the 6-color work begun in the 1930's by Stebbins and others, using U, V (for violet), B, G, R, and I combinations. Work of this kind begins increasingly to approximate to direct photoelectric measurement of the spectrum.

Indeed the information to be gained from relatively high spectral resolution is so great that systems using dozens of sharply discrete and narrow filter bands, and others which simply sweep an actual spectrum with a photocell, are now being used. However it remains difficult to get something for nothing—in such cases not only does it take longer to obtain more different color readings, but also the higher the spectral resolution the narrower each frequency band must be, hence the brighter must be the star in order to present the system with enough light for it to respond accurately. Work on fainter stars is thus generally limited to broad-band systems such as the *UBV*.

Photocell.   The heart of any photoelectric system is the light-sensitive device, or photocell. Earlier cells were very simple, consisting of an evacuated tube containing a photosensitive cathode and a positively charged anode to draw off the electrons liberated by photons striking the cathode. Kron has shown that even today the best of such cells, with proper amplifiers, are almost competitive with later types.

But photometry really became practical for the average astronomer with the development of the photomultiplier during the Second World War. Surfaces can be made which, upon being struck by an energetic electron, will erupt five to ten electrons. If beyond a photocathode, an array of such surfaces is properly laid out in a tube, and each is given a higher positive voltage than the former, a single original photoelectron becomes a multiplying cascade with millions of electrons finally reaching the last collecting anode. Such internal amplification is relatively noise-free and remarkably easy to achieve, requiring only the appropriate voltage supplies to the various anodes which can be provided as simply as with a stack of hearing-aid batteries.

Photocells, even of the same type and made by the same manufacturer, differ very widely in sensitivity, color response, and noise level. If possible one should normally test five or ten in order to select a really good one. The importance of this can be illustrated by translating photocell sensitivity into equivalent telescope sizes. The equivalence follows because in specifying the limit of a given photometric system we are really interested only in the number of photoelectrons produced per unit time for a given stellar magnitude. If one wishes to study fainter stars, he can either obtain a bigger telescope to pick up more light in the first place, or he can accomplish the same result by making more efficient use of the light from the original telescope with a more efficient photocell. Obtaining a cell ten times as sensitive as the one previously in use permits work on stars 2.5 mag. fainter; it is also equivalent to using the old cell with a telescope 3.3 times larger in aperture.

Ultimate limits exist for photocells in the sense that one can never reach more than 100 per cent quantum efficiency, where each incident photon liberates a photoelectron. Present routine cells have 1 to 20 per cent efficiencies, while experimental cells have approached 50 per cent. By comparison, photographic emulsions are rarely better than 0.1 per cent efficient and are normally far worse.

Since the cost of telescopes rises roughly with the cube of their apertures, it is clear why the economics of the situation speak plainly for increased research on photosensitive devices. To double the light-collecting ability of the 200-inch telescope would now cost about eight times the price of a 200-inch—that is, a 400-inch might well cost more than $100,000,000. Only a tiny fraction of this investment, if put into photocell improvement, might yield an equivalent gain. Ultimately the bigger telescope will be needed as well, but at the moment the better cells should be faster, easier, and cheaper to obtain.

Amplifier. Even the million-fold photocurrents from photomultipliers amount typically only to tiny fractions of a microampere, requiring still further amplification if the output is to be conveniently registered. Here a choice among DC, AC, or pulse-counting amplifiers enters.

The earliest photometer amplifiers were DC systems. Although requring considerable care in design and construction to insure stability and linearity, several very successful designs are currently available. DC techniques remain the most popular even today.

Many workers have experimented with various devices for chopping the photocurrent at some controlled frequency, so that this signal frequency can be amplified using AC techniques. AC amplifiers are somewhat simpler to build, stabilize, and linearize, but they suffer from the inherent difficulty of having to cut off with the chopper a part of the signal during each cycle. This represents a direct loss of information, leading to only 0.7 of the signal-to-noise ratio of an otherwise equivalent DC system.

After the Second World War, pulse-counting techniques rapidly became available. In these, each photoelectron produces a separate pulse which is counted. Such instruments are readily available com-

mercially, share the theoretical advantage of DC work and have
the additional properties of permitting some discrimination against
spurious secondary (rather than optically initated) electrons and of
putting out the information directly in a form most suited to statistical
analysis. In practice the advantages are usually only worth the expense
and effort for systems producing a large amount of data or for work
near the limit of faintness for a given telescope-photometer combination.

Recorder.   Recorders are rather expensive. Some professionals have
preferred, and many amateurs may still wish, to take direct visual
readings of an ordinary meter during observation. If in addition to
the observer, another person reads the meter, he can be partially
reducing the night's run while it is being taken. But recorders have
certain undeniable virtues, chiefly the ease with which one person
can obtain the records and their permanence for later analysis and
checking.

The ultimate in recording is the readout of digitized, or pulse-
counted, data directly into computer cards or tape, and the subsequent
analysis of such records by electronic computers. In this way the data
need not be touched by human hands until the final corrected magnitudes and colors are disgorged.

GENERAL PRINCIPLES OF PHOTOELECTRIC OBSERVING

Broadly speaking, photometric observations fall into perhaps four
principal categories as far as their purposes are concerned.

In the beginning observations are usually groping and exploratory.
We must have a general body of information before we can even make
useful classifications and theories. This exploratory, then taxonomic,
approach in photometric astronomy probably passed its peak a decade
ago. By now we know most of the principal kinds of interesting objects
which can be observed, although undoubtedly major surprises still
remain, especially among objects of small amplitude of light variation
and among relations involving only very subtle differences of color
and magnitude.

Second, even after a particular phenomenon or type of star is well understood, one wants to add more specific examples to the class, to understand better its validity and limits. Much of modern photometry is of this nature—search for and classification of more variables, study of additional star clusters, etc.

A third major type of use of photoelectric observations is the continual monitoring of objects of already known specific nature and behavior (normally variable stars) in order to build up the body of information about their consistency which will ultimately lead both to better theories about them and to the ability to check such theories. For example, we could profit from nearly continuous observation of some well-known variables such as β Lyrae or ε Aurigae. This remains an almost limitless field of activity for both amateurs and professionals, although by its nature this activity favors the amateur side.

Finally, observations can be directed sharply and specifically toward observing a relatively unique object or event or toward answering a specific orbital or astrophysical question at least to a certain level of precision. Many of the professional papers on photometry tend in this direction, although there is no inherent reason why skilled amateurs, especially if they can establish a working relation with a professional astronomer or observatory, cannot also engage in such activity.

From another point of view—that of the observer—there are two kinds of photometry, depending on the attitude he adopts toward extinction. Absolute photometry relies on knowledge or assumption of extinction coefficients and reduces each observation separately for extinction. Differential photometry, best applicable to variable stars, relies strictly on comparison of a variable with one or more immediately adjacent comparison stars known not to be variable. If a comparison star is close enough in position and color, and if readings on it are taken often enough, presumably any atmospheric effects on the variable are nearly identical to those on the comparison; hence a simple running difference of their magnitudes eleminates all first-order extinction effects. Of these two methods absolute photometry is used more in the western part of the United States where skies are better (some workers even assuming the same value of extinction for any good clear night). Absolute photometry must also be used whenever one needs to "tie in" a star with one of the standard sequences. Differential photometry is better adapted to the more varied observing conditions of midwest and east, where it nearly circumvents extinction problems. Most variable-star work is done differentially and can be successful for some purposes through otherwise very poor skies.

By now many purely photoelectric standard magnitude sequences have been set up over the sky. As a consequence practically no one ever now attempts to measure absolutely the amount of light coming from a star—rather, the unknown is compared with several stars of similar brightness whose magnitudes are already well established in a standard sequence. The importance of good magnitude sequences is underlined by a spectacular discovery made around 1954 when new, improved photomultipliers and techniques were used with the 200-inch telescope to push certain magnitude sequences down well below twentieth magnitude. Since photoelectric work is inherently linear, it was easy to maintain the Pogson ratio over the entire range from naked-eye stars on down. But around eighteenth to twentieth magnitudes, it was found that older photographic magnitudes departed from a Pogson scale by up to a magnitude. As a consequence, the older photographic workers had called twentieth magnitude galaxies nineteenth—and since distance estimates are normally made from brightness measures, this corresponded to assuming that galaxies in this magnitude range were $\sqrt{2.5} = 1.6$ times closer than they really are. This was one of three major errors in older work on distant galaxies, the total effect of which had been to make the observable universe seem about eight times smaller than it really is. These errors had grave effects on cosmology for a generation of astronomical work, leading to many false ideas concerning the nature of the metagalaxy.

OBJECTS AND USES OF PHOTOMETRY

While certain applications have already been touched on, this section summarizes the principal uses to which photometry can be put in the present state of astronomy. Some of these are particularly adapted to amateur work.

Standard Sequences

Fundamental magnitude standards now exist over all ranges of brightness, but there remains need for accurate secondary standard sequences in all parts of the sky. Such sequences are especially useful for calibrating photographic exposures and for providing comparison stars for variables. A particular application of interest to amateurs is the AAVSO's long list of variables kept under visual check by amateurs. More and better photoelectric comparison star sequences for the present variables and for new variables to be added would significantly improve the accuracy and value of this work.

Stellar Distances

A refined version of the method Huyghens pioneered is now basic to most distance determinations. It hinges on our being able in some way to estimate the total amount of light radiated by a star. This quantity, called *absolute magnitude,* is defined as the apparent magnitude which the star would have if put at a distance of 10 parsecs.

It then follows from our general magnitude equation that the apparent magnitude (m) at any distance (d) compares with the absolute magnitude (M) as

$$M = m + 5 - 5 \log d$$

(in this equation M and m must be in magnitudes and d in parsecs).

To derive this equation, consider the apparent intensity I_1 of a star having apparent magnitude m_1 at a distance d in parsecs. Imagine bringing it to 10 parsecs distance where its apparent intensity and magnitude become I_2 and m_2. Since the apparent intensity of a light varies with the inverse square of its distance,

$$\frac{I_1}{I_2} = \frac{10^2}{d^2} \quad ,$$

whence, from the definition of magnitudes,

$$2.5 \log \frac{10^2}{d^2} = m_2 - m_1 \quad .$$

But m_1, the apparent magnitude at distance d, is nothing but the actual apparent magnitude m; likewise, m_2, the apparent magnitude at 10 parsecs, is just the definition of absolute magnitude M. Substitution of these in the magnitude definition, and clearing, gives the magnitude-distance relation above.

To measure m for any star is simply a matter of photometry. An estimate of M for individual stars can come from other photometric clues including intrinsic variation, eclipsing binary studies, and some forms of spectrophotometry. Thus in many contexts d can be determined by purely photoelectric readings.

Color-Magnitude Arrays

One of the most important events in the history of astronomy was the discovery half a century ago, by Hertzsprung in Denmark and Russell at Princeton, that when the absolute magnitudes (true bright-ness) of stars are plotted against their spectral types (surface tempera-ture), most of the points fall on a *main sequence* (Fig. 1–6). We now know that slightly after its birth, each star settles down to a long stable adult life of converting hydrogen to helium in the deep interior. Such stars define the main sequence—the exact place of each star on the main sequence being determined by its mass (and composition). Low-mass, small-size, low-temperature, faint stars lie at the lower right; high-mass, large-size, hot, and enormously brighter stars fall toward the upper left. As stars approach old age, they move off the main sequence, first toward the upper right, finally cascading down into the lower white dwarf portion of the diagram (Fig. 1–7). Much can be learned about individual stars by placing them on such a diagram; even more follows from such studies of clusters.

The principal trouble with the older forms of Herzsprung-Russell diagrams was the difficulty of getting sufficiently reliable and clearly resolved information on absolute magnitudes and spectral classes. The usefulness of such diagrams skyrocketed when it was realized that accurate photometry could provide both coordinates for individual clusters of stars. It is only necessary to plot one of the magnitudes (usually the visual) against the color index. So simple a method works because in a cluster, where the stars are all at essentially the same distance from us, relative apparent magnitudes are the same as relative absolute magnitudes; further the method works because

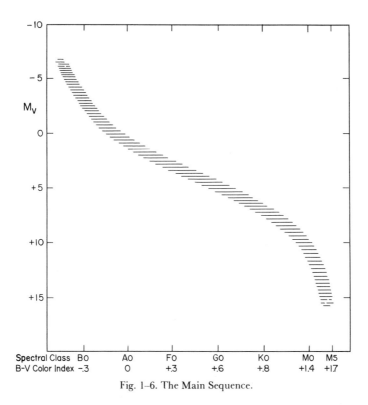

Fig. 1–6. The Main Sequence.

color index serves to measure surface temperature about as well as does spectral class. Used with the biggest telescopes and judiciously combined with photographic methods, this technique has given most of our present observational knowledge of stellar evolution and of ages of objects in the Milky Way.

Satisfactory work on color-magnitude arrays is demanding and specialized; nevertheless even modest telescopes probably could do useful work on unusual classes of objects. For example, there may be some tendency for stars to form in sheets or chains in certain parts of the sky under some conditions; color-magnitude studies offer an opportunity to establish or disprove the existance of such units.

Interstellar Absorption

Starlight is attenuated not only by extinction in the earth's atmosphere but also by interstellar grains, mainly of the small size of particles

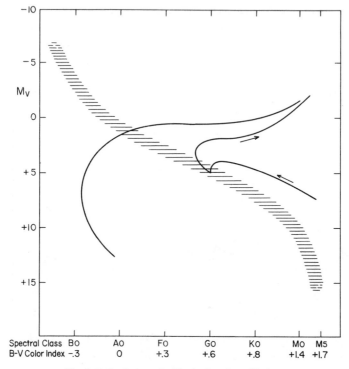

Fig. 1–7. Evolution of a Single Star from Birth to
White Dwarf.

making up cigarette smoke (about 10^{-5} cm). While some true absorption probably occurs, most of the effect is one of scattering of the light to the side or even back in the direction from which it came. This scattering action is strongly dependent on wavelength, affecting blue light most markedly and accordingly allowing the red light preferentially to get through. The over-all effect is thus to make the star appear redder than its true color as well as dimmer than it should be. When independent criteria (e.g., spectral classification) make it possible to specify the expected color, comparison with the measured color permits estimation of the amount of excess reddening (the "color excess") and from this the total amount of absorption. Careful work shows that, for the UBV system, the total absorption in V magnitudes is about three times the color excess in B-V. This method is normally valuable only in conjunction with an extensive body of spectral information, but can be a tool of very great power.

Polarization

The interstellar matter, in addition to reddening the light, also imposes a slight degree of polarization. The cause is still obscure, although presumably dependent on particular orientation of elongated grains by weak galactic magnetic fields.

This polarization is hard to detect and to measure reliably, but a large amount of such work remains to be done by medium-sized telescopes to supplement the existing lists of stars with known polarization, and to map out more of the magnetic field pattern of the galaxy.

Variable Stars

By far the most frequent application of photometry is in the study of variable stars. In this context variation is defined as a detectable change of magnitude occurring over a reasonable period of time, usually less than centuries. While a few variables are listed which have amplitudes of variation as small as several hundredths of a magnitude, for the vast majority the amplitudes are greater than 0.5 mag., since photographic detection has been necessary. By these criteria, more than 15,000 variables are now known. The total number of detectable variables must be vastly greater; it can be estimated from the following statistics. Of the 8,600 stars visually brighter than 6.5 mag. about 1.4 per cent are known to vary, and at least 10 per cent have been suspected to vary. Of a third of a million BD (*Bonner Durchmusterung*) Catalogue stars brighter than about 10.5 mag., nearly $\frac{1}{4}$ per cent are known and 1 per cent are suspected to vary. These figures suggest that the efficiency of detection has decreased with decreasing apparent brightness of the stars and that very careful work would reveal detectable variability in several per cent of stars of any magnitude whatever. That is, brighter than eighth visual magnitude one might expect 1,500 variables; tenth magnitude, 10,000 variables; twelfth magnitude, 70,000 variables; fourteenth magnitude, 420,000 variables; etc. And these figures take no real account of extremely minute variations which may prove to accompany many, even most, stars. While there is presumably a point of diminishing returns in studies of this kind, clearly an almost indefinite future remains for photoelectric work to improve the classification and knowledge of the variables now catalogued, to check the stars suspected of variability, and to search for new variables among various classes and groupings of stars. Since stars brighter than tenth magnitude are easy objects for ten- or twelve-inch reflectors, a very large number of variables lie within reach of amateur equipment.

Several general classes of variables are recognized. In the first, or *extrinsic*, the variation is imposed on a star's light from without, by something getting between us and the star. But a great many stars vary from internal, or *intrinsic*, causes. These in turn fall into two principal groups. *Explosive* variables take many forms ranging from relatively mild and repetitive eruptions to total disruption of the star. *Pulsating* stars alternately swell and shrink, although their light changes arise most directly from changes in surface temperature associated with the pulsation rather than from the change of size itself.

Extrinsic variables. Some stars may show irregular fading or flaring caused in part by patches of obscuring interstellar matter drifting in front of or falling into them (T Tauri variables), or possibly even caused by opaque matter forming in their high atmospheres (R Corona Borealis variables). But the principal extrinsic variables are the binaries.

More than half of all stars are probably associated with others in binary or multiple combinations. Occasionally our line of sight happens to lie almost exactly in the orbital plane of a binary. In such a case each star will successively eclipse the other by passing across its face.

Eclipsing binaries are treated extensively in later chapters; here we should only note that most of our direct observational information concerning stellar sizes, masses, surface brightnesses, and many other properties has come from the study of binaries. The photometry of eclipsing pairs makes high demands on the observer, since errors of as little as a hundredth of a magnitude at critical parts of the eclipse cycle can change significantly the interpretation of the star.

Exploding stars.   Probably at least once and perhaps quite frequently near the end of the active life of a typical star, physical conditions in its interior reach a state of extreme instability; the star then blows some of its substance into space accompanied by a tremendous flashing up in brightness.

Supernovae are the most spectacular of such stellar explosions, reaching up to hundreds of millions of solar brightnesses for a few weeks. However bright supernovae are seen only at intervals of centuries in a galaxy such as ours.

Regular or *classical novae* occur more frequently—perhaps thirty per year in our galaxy. Accurate photometry of the long declines of novae would certainly be worthwhile.

Some novae even have been observed to repeat their outbursts after several decades of quiescence; these offer at least a chance for observations never yet achieved, namely accurate photometry of a nova on the rise. Old novae also show remarkable behavior while at minimum. Thus Nova Herculis is a binary with the remarkably short period of 4.5 hours, further, one of its components is apparently a pulsating star with the period 1.184 minutes! Finally, some dwarf novae have rather regular outbursts every few weeks or months.

Flare stars, though they show unpredictable brightenings, probably belong in a category other than the novae—that of reasonably normal stars having magnetically induced surface flare activity similar to that of the sun.

Pulsating stars. Most intrinsic variables fall in what has been called the great sequence, consisting of stars rythmically changing brightness, some as rapidly as a few hours, some requiring several years or more. With only a few exceptions, the interval from one maximum to the next (the period) defines very well and unambiguously the class of the the star.

The best-known types of intrinsic variables are the RR Lyrae stars (periods ranging from about 0.2 days to slightly over one day) and the classical Cepheids (periods from around two days to about 100 days). The principal value of these stars lies in the measurement of stellar distances. From the period of variation of such a star we can estimate closely its true (absolute) magnitude; with the photometer we also determine its apparent magnitude; these two items of information, sometimes supplemented by information about interstellar absorption, suffice to estimate the distance to the star and to any cluster or galaxy containing the star.

Figure 1–8 shows on an H-R diagram the presently accepted classes of intrinsic variables. They seem to consist of well-marked evolutionary stages of transient instability, lasting perhaps millions of years, but the intervals of pulsation can represent at most only a tiny fraction of the

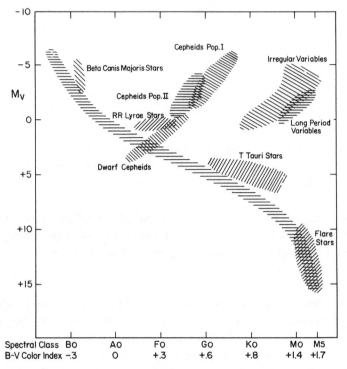

Figure 1-8. Approximate domains on the H-R diagram of some of the principal presently recognized classes of intrinsic variables.

billions of years of total life of a typical star—otherwise a higher proportion of stars would be variable.

Variable star programs of particular interest for amateurs with photoelectric equipment might be the systematic analysis of stars suspected to vary (see *Catalogue of Stars Suspected of Variability*, Moscow, 1951), and the search for stars of small amplitude and/or extremely fast variation, which have been missed almost entirely in earlier photographic searches. The latter search program should turn up many binaries with grazing eclipses, some "ellipsoidal stars" (binaries with one component too small or faint to be detected except from its shape-distorting action on the primary), magnetic variables, old novae, dwarf cepheids, irregular red variables, and probably unknown types of objects.

Solar System Objects

While a bit difficult to make, photometric observations of *asteroids* nearly always reveal small variations having periods of five or six hours, associated with rotation of the asteroid. Many hundreds of asteroids are within range of medium-sized telescopes, and a major compaign could improve our knowledge of such variations.

Comets, while not always available, show remarkable and unpredictable changes of brightness which could be followed by photometers equipped with large diaphragms. This is one of the more important projects available to amateurs.

The *outer planets* have been suspected to show substantial if slow changes in brightness; many years of careful monitoring might give information bearing on either solar or planetary changes.

Extremely accurate photoelectric *lunar occultation timings* still have substantial value in checking the motion of the moon and the rotation rate of the Earth. This problem requires only a small telescope and photometer, but a good fast recorder and means of registering WWV or equivalently accurate times to the order of hundredths of a second.

The above possibilities are not exhaustive. For example, little work has been done on accurate photometry of auroras—the brightness per unit area of sky in the various colors and the types and speeds of variation. Also scintillation can be regarded as an intriguing scientific problem rather than a nuisance, with specialized equipment set up to measure it. Meteorological information or techniques of substantial value may come from such work.

SUMMARY

Originating as a stepchild of classical astronomy, useful only as an adjunct in stellar identification, photometry has become one of the major branches of modern astronomy, with applications to nearly all classes of celestial objects. Other than in certain specialized problems, astronomical photometry now means photoelectric photometry, where routine accuracies of about .02 mag. are expected for each observation, but where an order of magnitude of greater accuracy can usually be obtained when truly necessary.

Variable stars will normally occupy amateur or small-scale professional photoelectric observatories, but a rich array of other applications exists. Variable stars alone can provide a generation of work for small telescopes equipped with good modern photometers, while the super-photocells and photometers ultimately available will make twelve-inch telescopes equal to present thirty-inch ones in limiting magnitude, greatly extending their useful life.

In short, nature has not yet set the limits on what can be achieved in astronomical photometry—the future is still bounded primarily by our energy, our ingenuity, and our insight into astronomy.

CHAPTER 2

Photoelectric Photometers

BY A. D. CODE

Washburn Observatory
University of Wisconsin

INTRODUCTION

In the detailed design of a photoelectric photometer the professional astronomer takes into consideration the astronomical problem he wishes to attack with the instrument as well as the type of telescope on which the photometer is to be used. In general the amateur must endeavor to keep his photometer relatively simple and economical. This however does not preclude first investigating those features which influence the selection of an optimum photoelectric system. The relation between the light emitted by a star and the final pointer reading or record obtained by the photometer is not a simple one. In Figure 2–1 the complete optical and electrical path is illustrated schematically. We should like to obtain information on the stellar radiation possibly modified by the intervening interstellar medium. However the transmission of the Earth's atmosphere changes this radiation considerably. The transparency varies with wavelength and with the zenith distance of the star, as well as varying from night to night and possibly hour to hour. The method of dealing with the atmospheric extinction is discussed in Chapter 4. It is also the Earth's atmosphere that is responsible in part for the brightness of the sky background and, most important of all, for the size of the seeing tremor disk of the star. The spectral distribution of the light is further modified by the transmission of the telescope optics, while the precision with which we can guide upon the stellar image is determined principally by the quality of the equatorial mounting and telescope drive. In the focal plane of the telscope a diaphragm is inserted to pass only the light of the star to be measured. The smaller this diaphragm is, the fainter the sky background and hence the fainter the limiting magnitude of the system. The size of this diaphragm is determined by the focal length of the telescope, the size of the seeing disk and the steadiness of the telescope mounting and drive. The light is then analyzed by passing it through some form of spectral analyzer. In a simple photometer it is usually a glass color filter which determines the spectral region being observed. The radiation is then intercepted by a field lens or Fabry lens designed to focus an image of the telescope objective on the detector's sensitive element. The most satisfactory detector in the blue region of the spectrum is a photomultiplier such as the 1P21. This tube requires a stabilized high-voltage supply providing approximately one thousand volts. The signal from the photomultiplier is then sent to an amplifier. A DC amplifier with the maximum current gain of the order of 10^6 is generally satisfactory. The output of the amplifier is then read on a meter or recorded on a paper chart recorder. If the system is properly designed the final pointer reading bears a linear relationship to the intensity of stellar radiation falling on the telescope objective. In addition to the elements shown in Figure 2–1 suitable eyepieces must be provided for identifying the proper star and for centering this star in the diaphragm. If one wishes to push this system to its limits of detectability it is desirable to provide for refrigeration of the photomultiplier and to introduce means by which it is practical to average the photomultiplier current over fairly long intervals of time. One such technique is the use of pulse counters rather than current measuring amplifiers. Since counters of sufficient dynamic range are relatively expensive, we shall not consider them here. In the following sections we shall consider the elements of a photoelectric photometer system starting with the limitations imposed by the telescope itself. We shall next consider the construction of the photometer assembly and finally the associated electronic components.

TELESCOPES

In photoelectric photometry the function of the telescope is to collect as much light from a single object as possible and focus this on the photosensitive detector. As a light collector, therefore, no requirements are placed upon the off-axis image quality. Obviously the larger the telescope the more light it will collect. Useful observations may be obtained, however, with a telescope as small as five inches. Although we can expect to go two magnitudes fainter with a twelve-inch telescope and three and a half magnitudes fainter with a twenty-four-inch in-

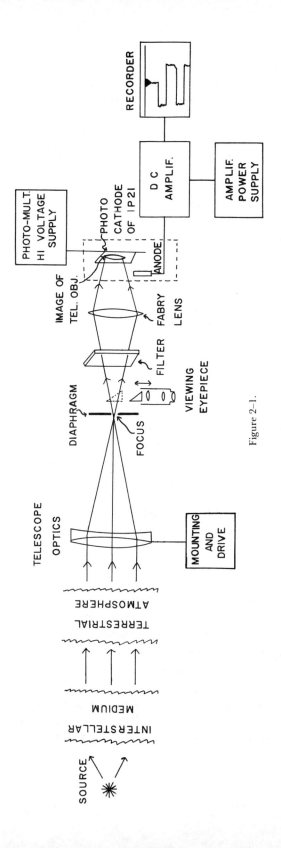

Figure 2–1.

strument, there is no simple relation that gives the limiting magnitude obtainable with a photoelectric photometer for a given size telescope. This depends upon the time spent, the accuracy desired and the quality of seeing, as well as the instrumental parameters. Indeed it should be possible to measure a sixteenth magnitude star with a five-inch telescope. In addition to requiring an excellent photometer, however, this implies the ability to set and guide for long periods of time on an object that is not visible to the eye. This additional requirement of off-set guiding increases the complexity of the photometer and puts high demands on the telescope mounting and drive. A realistic objective for the amateur to aim for in constructing a photoelectric photometer is an instrument capable of measuring any star that can be seen well enough to be centered in the photometer diaphragm.

In general the smallest size of the on-axis image will not be set by the telescope but by the atmospheric seeing. It is a rare night when 99 per cent of the light is to be found within two seconds of arc; more often the image size is three or four seconds of arc or greater. In a small telescope a sharp image showing the diffraction rings of the telescope may often be seen. This image moves about in the focal plane, with excursions of several seconds of arc. Thus the time average of the intensity distribution in the focal plane corresponds to the intensity distribution in the images formed by a large telescope. The transition in the appearance of the image as a function of the size of the telescope depends upon the particular night but occurs at about a twelve-inch aperture. The larger scintillation exhibited by a small telescope is apparent in the output of the photoelectirc photometer, where it shows in the form of rapid fluctuations. This noisy record nevertheless shows a well-defined average.

A reflecting telescope is to be preferred for photoelectric photometry, both because of the absence of chromatic aberration and because of the higher ultraviolet efficiency. The effect of chromatic aberration on the performance of a typical refractor is shown in Figure 2–2. The solid curve shows the variation in focal length with wavelength for an achromat corrected in the visual, while the broken curve presents the image size if the telescope is focused in the visual. In the example shown, namely an F-20 refractor, the image size becomes appreciably larger than the average seeing disk by 4,500 Angstroms. Either the focus must be changed when observing in the ultraviolet or a larger diaphragm employed for all observations. If the light were focused directly onto the photocathode the change in spot size would show up in a change in effective sensitivity of the photomultiplier. A field lens or Fabry lens is usually used, however, and this insures that the image on the photocathode will always remain the same size and in the same position. This is discussed in more detail below.

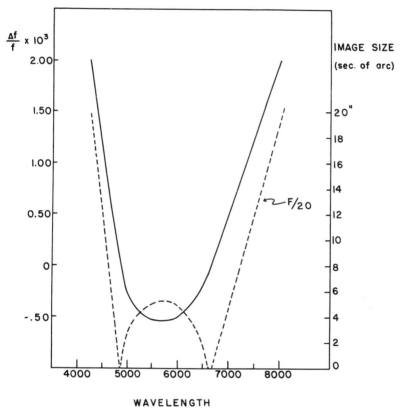

WAVELENGTH

Figure 2–2.

The relative efficiency of reflectors and refractors is illustrated in Figure 2–3, where the heavy solid curve shows the transmission of a typical achromatic refractor as a function of wavelength. The broken curve is the reflectivity of a good aluminum coating. The spectral band passes for the UBV photometric system are described in the next section. It is clear that the transmission cut off in the ultraviolet of the refractor seriously effects the U magnitude determinations.

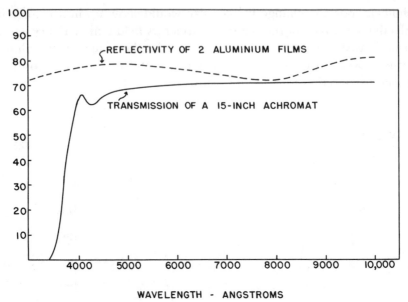

WAVELENGTH - ANGSTROMS

Figure 2–3.

Despite the two drawbacks of a refractor discussed above, many important and useful investigations can and have been carried out with refractors. On the other hand very little of significance has come from telescopes that are poorly mounted. Indeed the rigidity of the mounting, the precision of the drive, and the ease of setting of a telescope are the most important factors in assessing the usefulness and quality of the instrument, although even poor mountings have been overcome by the observer blessed with skill and determination.

The greatest demands are placed upon the telescope drive and mounting when it is desirable to use as small a photometer diaphragm as possible, either to isolate a single star in a crowded field or to minimize the light from the sky background. In practice it is found that a diaphragm about twice the size of the seeing tremor disk is required to accept safely all the light during an average exposure time. Thus on nights of good seeing the guiding accuracy of the telescope should be of the order of one second of arc, a precision difficult to attain. A precision of five seconds of arc does not, in general, seriously limit the usefulness of the telescope under the conditions cited above and yet becomes a practical tolerance for the amateur telescope maker. The telescope drive should therefore track to about five seconds of arc over a period of ten to twenty minutes. It should be rigid enough so that winds and other disturbances are also limited to about a five second amplitude. Finally the flexure and vibration produced by the observer in actuating the filter slide and other photometer operations should quickly damp out or not exceed this same limit. If such performance is realized then a diaphragm as small as ten seconds of arc may be used on occasion and the sky background will be fainter than a sixteenth magnitude star.

The choice of F-ratio and the location of the focus is more a matter of convenience than one of performance. The photometer design is simplified if it is to operate in the less steeply converging bundle of, say, an F/15 rather than an F/5 telescope. In general it is easier to obtain the necessary rigidity at a Cassegrain focus than at a Newtonian. Most observers, therefore, prefer a Cassegrain reflector operating at about F/15.

Before attempting to design a photoelectric photometer it is necessary to know the F-ratio of the telescope and the scale or number of seconds of arc per millimeter in the focal plane. In the following section we shall discuss two photometer designs one suitable for small F-ratios of the order of F/5 and one more adaptable to F/10 or larger. The F-ratio determines the space available behind the focal plane diaphragm for mounting filters, eyepieces, a field lens, and photocell. The scale determines the linear size of the diaphragm holes required to accept a given angular patch of the sky as well as the type of eyepieces required.

The F-ratio, given by the ratio of telescope focal length to objective diameter, conveniently expresses the rate at which the bundle of light will fan out away from the focus. For example, a ten-inch mirror of fifty-inch focal length produces an F/5 bundle. Thus if one-inch filters are to be used they must be placed within five inches of the focus. It would be safer to illuminate only $\frac{1}{2}$ to $\frac{1}{4}$ inch of the filter, in which case they should be located within $2\frac{1}{2}$ and $1\frac{1}{4}$ inches respectively. On the other hand too small a spot on the filter is undesirable for then a grain of dust or a defect in the glass filter would be serious. Therefore, in an F/16 bundle the filter should probably be located about four inches outside of the focus where the spot of light would be $\frac{1}{4}$ inches in diameter. Thus in judging the position and diameter of lenses and filters it should be kept in mind that at a distance S from the focus the light bundle will have a diameter d given by the relation F-ratio $= S/d$.

The scale at the focus of a telescope is determined by the focal length *f*. If *f* is measured in inches then the scale in seconds of arc per millimeter is

$$\text{Scale} = \frac{8,000}{f} \text{ sec/mm}$$

If the scale at the focus of a telescope is uncertain it may be quickly determined by trailing a star across the field viewed through an eyepiece with a suitable reticle or through an aperture of known linear dimensions. If a star on the equator is chosen the diurnal drift will trail the star at a rate of 15 seconds of arc per second of time.

For the 10-inch F/5 telescope discussed above the scale is 8,000/50 = 160 sec/mm. This means that a one millimeter diaphragm is 160 sec in diameter and a 10-second diaphragm is only 1/16 mm in diameter or approximately 0.0025 inches, a size which is exceedingly difficult to make. A 16-inch F/20 Cassegrain telescope, on the other hand, has a focal length of 320 inches and therefore a scale of 25 sec/mm. A 10-sec diaphragm in this case is 0.4 mm, or about 0.016 inches which can be drilled with a number 78 drill.

The amateur generally will have little choice but to use the telescope he has available. He can improve, of course, the mounting and drive with a little ingenuity if it falls short of the necessary performance. The effective focal length may be increased by a factor of two or three by the use of a negative lens in the converging bundle. Most amateurs know of this lens as a Barlow lens. It serves the same purpose as a Cassegrain secondary mirror but does introduce some chromatic aberration and additional absorption in the ultraviolet.

The purpose of this discussion has been twofold; first to indicate the desirable characteristics of a telescope to be used for photoelectric photometry, and secondly to indicate those parameters that should be considered in designing the photometer. Whatever the telescope may be, however, a properly constructed system should be capable of measuring any star that can be clearly seen with the telescope.

PHOTOMETERS

The elements of a photoelectric photometer have already been illustrated in Figure 2–1. In this section we shall consider the photometer assembly up through the photomultiplier. In the final section we will discuss the electronic components.

Perhaps the simplest form of photometer is the type that makes use of a hinged photomultiplier box. This type is also well suited for use in rapidly converging light bundles as fast as F/3. This "swing back" photometer is illustrated in Figure 2–4. All components are mounted on a single flat plate. A slide containing the glass color filters is mounted in front of the focus. A diaphragm slide or alternatively a diaphragm wheel is mounted on the other side of the plate and is to be positioned in the focal plane. The photomultiplier housing is mounted on a second plate secured to the main plate by means of hinges and a simple latch. If the dark slide is closed, the photomultiplier may be swung back providing clear access to the focus without exposing the multiplier to room light. By placing the filter slide in a clear position and using a large diaphragm the field may be examined by an eyepiece that may simply be held by hand or more conveniently swung into place from a hinged mounting. When the appropriate diaphragm for observing is moved in the program star may be centered accurately by means of this eyepiece. The eyepiece is then swung back and the photomultiplier returned to its locked position. After inserting the proper filter observations may commence by opening the photomultiplier dark slide.

In laying out a design of a photometer for a particular telescope it would be well to start with a full scale drawing. First draw in the optical axis and the converging bundle from the telescope. The rays will diverge beyond the focus 1 inch for each F-inches, where F is the appropriate F-number. Next select a satisfactory filter position. Let us assume that we wish to illuminate an area $\frac{1}{4}$ inch in diameter on the filter. In an F/5 bundle the filters should then be located $1\frac{1}{4}$ inches in front of the focus; for an F/10, $2\frac{1}{2}$ inches in front. A 1 inch square filter makes a convenient size for mounting. The stock size for glass filters is 2×2 from which four filters may be cut, although for a small additional charge the manufacturer will provide 1×1 filters. For general purpose photometry you will want to be able to make three color measurements similar to the UBV system. The U or ultraviolet filter is a Corning 9863 glass which, in combination with an aluminized mirror and a 1P21 photomultiplier, gives an effective wavelength in the neighborhood of 3,550 Å. The B, or blue, filter uses a Corning 5030 glass and a Schott GG13 to cut off the transmission of the blue filter short of 3,700 Å. The effective wavelength of this combination is about 4,250 Å.

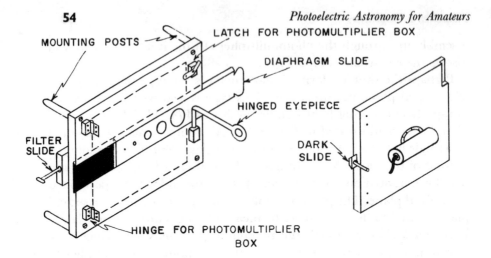

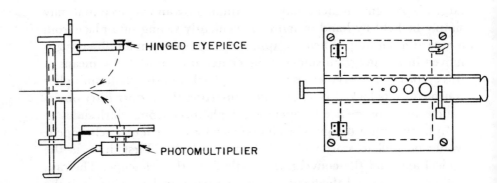

Figure 2–4.

The yellow filter used for the V magnitude is a Corning 3384 which is limited on the red side by the falling sensitivity of the 1P21. The effective wavelength of the V filter is around 5,450 Å. Other filters including interference filters may be desirable for specific programs and for use with other types of photoelectric devices. Sources for these filters are given in Chapter 3, and methods of constructing filter slides and retaining rings are indicated in the drawings and photographs.

The next step is to determine the scale of the telescope as described in the preceding section, and select diaphragm sizes. Let us assume for example that the telescope is a 10-inch F/10 with a focal length therefore of 100 inches. The scale is 80 sec of arc per mm. Table 2–1 suggests some appropriate diaphragm sizes for such an instrument. The holes may be

Table 2-1

Size of hole in sec of arc	Size of hole in mm	Size of hole in inches	Numbered drill size
81.1″	1.015	0.040	#60
40.6″	0.508	0.020	#76
27.4″	0.343	0.0135	#80
10.0″	0.127	0.005	Pin prick

drilled into a brass plate of, say, 1/16-inch thickness. In order to avoid a tunnel effect, however, they may first be counterbored on the side that is to be placed away from the objective. In order to make round holes of the proper diameter it is best first to drill a pilot hole with a smaller drill when possible. This is not possible for the number 80 drill since this is the smallest size numbered drill. These drills are very fine and care must be exercised to avoid breaking them. Very small round holes may be produced by pricking aluminum foil with the point of a very sharp needle against a hard metal backing using a twisting motion. Make a number of holes and select the best after examination with an eyepiece. The aluminum foil may then be cut out and cemented over a larger hole in the diaphragm slide. The most useful diaphragms will probably prove to be the 27 second and 40 second ones. In addition to these small diaphragms it should be possible to remove the slide completely or provide a hole at least ¾ inch in diameter for viewing the entire field in order to locate the program star.

In order to center a star in the diaphragm some method must be provided for illuminating the diaphragms. This may be done by edge lighting; even a flash light directed under the viewing eyepiece will work. Another technique is to illuminate the field by a light source located in the telescope tube. A ring of fluorescent paint around the diaphragm edge and illuminated by black light which is turned off during observations has been used. Do not use a radioactive phosphor, since the photomultiplier will see this as well as the star. Radioactive phosphors do however provide a useful artificial source and are used by many observers. A plate containing a good temperature-independent phosphor may be placed in the filter slide to provide a relatively constant light source to check the photometer for any change in sensitivity.

The next step is to locate the Fabry lens and photomultiplier on your drawing. The purpose of the Fabry lens is to project an image of the telescope objective on the photocathode. This is required since the sensitivity of the photocathode is not uniform and often shows variations of a factor of two or more from point to point. Without this field lens motion of the star within the diaphragm would result in motions of the spot of light on the photocathode and hence variations in sensitivity. The Fabry lens produces an image very similar to that seen when making a knife-edge test and remains fixed on the photocathode. Because the focal length of the Fabry lens is at most a few inches, we can generally regard the telescope objective as being at infinity. Therefore, the image of the telescope objective will be located very near the focus of the Fabry lens. Now the illuminated spot on the photocathode should be no greater than $\frac{1}{4}$ inch and unless adjustments are provided to center accurately on a specific high sensitivity spot on the photocathode the image should be no smaller than $\frac{1}{8}$ inch. The ratio of image spot size to telescope objective is essentially the same as the ratio of the focal length of the Fabry lens to the focal length of the objective. From this it follows that the spot size is

$$a = f/F$$

where a is the size of the image, f the focal length of the Fabry lens and F the F-ratio of the telescope. Therefore, for our F/10 telescope a Fabry lens with a focal length of $2\frac{1}{2}$ inches will give a $\frac{1}{4}$ inch image on the photocathode. The location of the Fabry lens is not critical: it may be located at any convenient distance behind the focus providing it will accept all the star light from the telescope. This means that it must be the size of the largest diaphragm used plus the additional fanning out of the divergent bundle. In our example of the swingback photometer the Fabry lens would be located quite close to the focus; about $\frac{1}{4}$ inch would leave ample room for the thickness of the swing back plate and a lens mounting ring. There are no great demands on the quality of the lens since a good image is not required; however, it should have reasonable ultraviolet transmission if it is not to effect the U filter response. Simple double convex crown or light flint lenses are quite satisfactory.

The photomultiplier must now be located so that the photocathode is at the focus of the Fabry lens. When using a 1P21 or a 931A the tube should be oriented so that the key on the tube socket pin faces the incident light. The photocathode of a 1P21 is then located approxi-

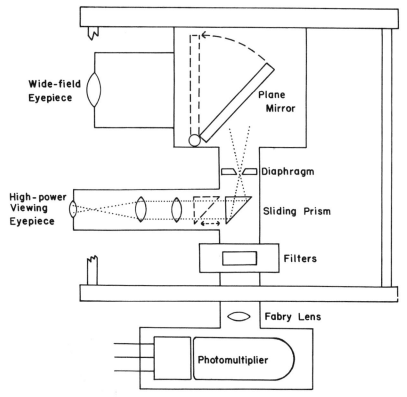

Figure 2–5.

mately 0.2 inches in front of the central axis of the tube. It is also inclined to the optical axis by approximately 45 degrees so that the imaging of the Fabry lens is not perfect. This is not serious, however.

Figure 2–5 illustrates a somewhat different type of photometer arrangement utilizing a sliding prism or mirror to view the star through the diaphragm. The prism is shown in the viewing position. The prism must be mounted in such a manner that it may be moved out of the beam when making the photometric measurements and returned again to the same position. This is most easily done by mounting the prism on the end of a tube that slides into the eyepiece tube by means of a knob protruding through a slot in the outer tube. The optical arrangement for this diaphragm-viewing eyepiece permits the use of a tube of any convenient length. The lens closest to the prism is focused on the diaphragm and therefore collimates the light if the total distance from

Figure 2–6. Diaphragm attachment for use with viewing eyepiece (with prism in place) or with photometer (with prism withdrawn). *b* is a view of section A--A of drawing *a*, showing prism in place for viewing. In this view the telescope would be attached at the top. *c*, three views of the viewing prism. *d*, the sliding diaphragm, with three apertures. *e*, the diaphragm assembly. *f*, the viewing eyepiece.

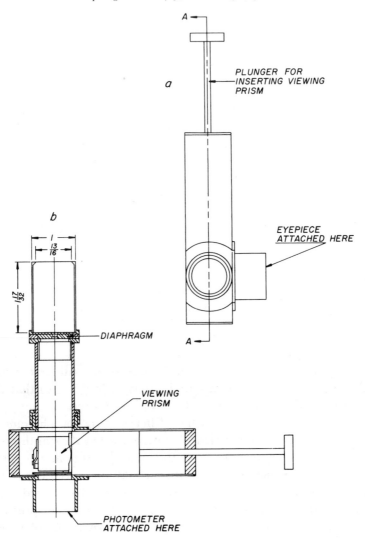

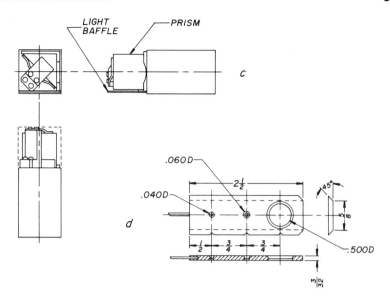

LIGHT
BAFFLE   PRISM

c

d

.060 D
.040 D
$2\frac{1}{2}$
45°
$\frac{5}{8}$
.500 D
$\frac{1}{2}$ $\frac{3}{4}$ $\frac{3}{4}$
$\frac{3}{32}$

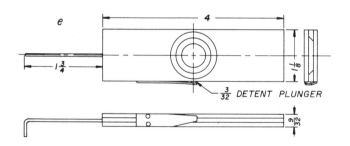

e

4
$1\frac{3}{4}$
$\frac{1}{8}$
$\frac{3}{32}$ DETENT PLUNGER
$\frac{9}{32}$

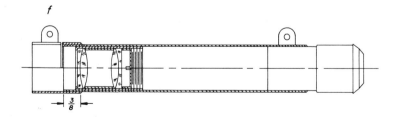

f

$\frac{3}{8}$

the diaphragm through the prism to the lens is equal to the focal length of this lens. Since the light rays are now parallel the second lens may be located at any convenient distance beyond the first. This relay lens system makes it possible to bring the viewing eyepiece well out beyond the photometer for easy access. The second lens is the same focal length as the first lens and therefore an image of the star and the diaphragm is formed behind the second lens at its focal point. This image is then viewed with a conventional eyepiece. When the prism is removed from the light beam the light passes through the filters and Fabry lens to the photocathode. Also shown in this figure is a large field-viewing eyepiece placed above the diaphragm slide. A large mirror is hinged so that it may be swung into the beam and reflect the field off to a wide-angle eyepiece as shown by the dotted lines. An Erfle eyepiece is ideal for this wide-field eyepiece. While the wide-field eyepiece is convenient for identifying and centering the program star it is not necessary if the telescope sets well or the finder is sufficiently large and properly aligned.

Figure 2–6 shows details on the construction of one form of diaphragm slide, viewing eyepiece, and filter slide. In this case all the diaphragm holes are drilled in a plate which slides from one position to another and is accurately positioned by precision detents. A simple slot into which one of a number of different size diaphragm plates may be inserted also proves very satisfactory. A simple photometer assembly may be constructed by the use of brass tubing soldered together. This is illustrated in the exploded view shown in Figure 2–7.

A photometer incorporating a wide field viewing eyepiece lends itself most easily to a box structure similar to that shown in Figure 2–8. This photometer is constructed of duraluminum plate and brass tubing and requires the use of a lathe and milling machine for its construction. A sturdy and satisfactory photometer may be constructed from wood or other structural materials. Figure 2–9 shows a photometer built by Donald West from balsa wood, cardboard, and epoxy. Indeed, by the use of epoxy any construction that can be made with paper, fiberglass, cardboard or wood can be converted to a solid structure by applying several coatings of epoxy which will gradually build up a glass-like surface of great strength.

The photomultiplier, however, should be mounted in a metal housing to provide electrical shielding. Occasionally a photomultiplier requires magnetic shielding as well, to prevent the earth's magnetic field from changing the multiplication as the telescope position is varied. It is the

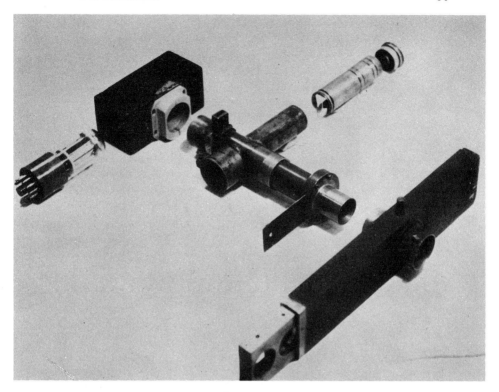

Figure 2–7.

rare case, however, when this effect is significant. The most important features in connection with the mounting of the photomultiplier are the care that is taken to maintain high electrical resistance between terminals and to ground and the rigidity of the mounting. The photomultiplier must be supported so that there is no significant flexure or motion of the tube relative to the Fabry lens. If the Fabry lens and photomultiplier are securely tied together mechanically the image of the telescope objective will remain fixed on the same part of the photocathode, unless there is large flexure between the photometer and telescope. The 1P21 may be mounted in a mica mold 11 Pin tube socket secured at right angles to the optical axis with the tube socket key facing the light. The method of wiring will be described in the next section.

The choice of the 1P21 photomultiplier is based on the fact that it has been used extensively by astronomers and has exceptionally high

Figure 2–8.

Figure 2–9.

quantum efficiency. Few other photomultipliers approach the efficiency of the 1P21, although many have lower noise and dark current and are more satisfactory optically. The 1P21 is about the size of an ordinary glass octal vacuum tube. The light enters the side of the tube and falls on a sloping photocathode as described previously. There now exist a number of comparable photomultipliers with end-on photocathodes that avoid this difficulty. The 1P21 possesses one distinct advantage for the amateur, however. It is electrically equivalent to a 931A photomultiplier, being simply a high performance 931A. The 931A currently costs $10., the 1P21, $60., and many of the other photomultipliers are priced above $100. The amateur would do well first to try out his system with a 931A; indeed it may prove sufficient for all the observing contemplated and it can happen that a 931A may be purchased that out-performs the average 1P21.

These photomultipliers are blue-sensitive, having a Cesium Antimony (CsSb) photocathode. This type of cathode is referred to in the literature as an S4 cathode. The wavelength sensitivity of an S4 surface in combination with the filters described before yield the U, B, and V band passes. An S4 surface can have a quantum efficiency in excess of 20 percent; that is, one electron on the average is ejected from the photosurface for every five incident photons. For comparison a Cesium silver or S1 surface, which is sensitive in the visual and near infrared as well, has a quantum efficiency of less than one percent and photographic films are less than one-tenth of a per cent efficient. It would be wise for the amateur to acquaint himself with the theory and performance of photoelectric devices as well as acquiring a knowledge of the detectors on the market.

For those more ambitious amateurs who wish to try to refrigerate their photomultipliers Figure 2–10 shows details of one form of cold box. The cooling is accomplished by radiation from the outer chamber containing dry ice or liquid nitrogen. The insulation is santocell, a powdery diatomatious earth, although the structurally more satisfactory styrafoam works as well. In order to prevent condensation on the window or the electrical connectors heaters are provided. The secret of a successful cold box is to make the inner chamber air tight and therefore water vapor tight so that condensation will not occur in the photomultiplier area.

Another refinement that some may wish to try is offset guiding for faint stars. For this purpose a guiding eyepiece must be provided that has calibrated X and Y motions. The faint star is centered in the diaphragm on the basis of measurement of its distance from a star bright enough to see, made on a photograph of the region of the sky. This bright star is then centered in the diaphragm. The guiding eyepiece then is moved until a suitable guide star is centered on the cross hairs. The calibrated X and Y motions of the guiding eyepiece are then offset by the previously measured displacement of the faint

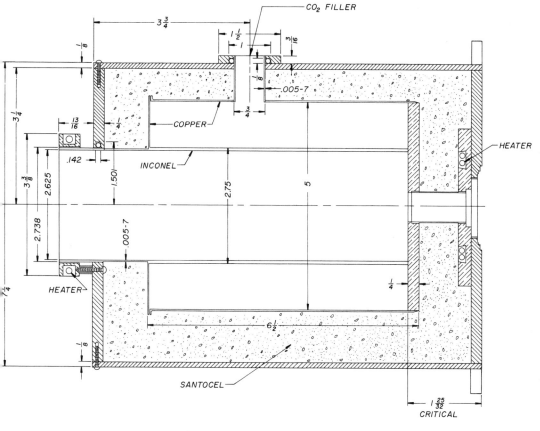

FULL SECTION

Figure 2–10.

star from the bright one. The telescope is then moved until the original guide star is centered in the guiding eyepiece. The faint star is then presumably in the center of the diaphragm. The construction of such an offset guidance mechanism requires considerable skill as does the mastery of the observing technique.

ELECTRONIC COMPONENTS

The photomultiplier incorporates both a photocell and a high gain current amplifier in one glass envelope. Light incident on the photo-cathode releases photoelectrons which are accelerated by the positive potential towards the first dynode with sufficient energy that each photoelectron is capable of releasing several secondary electrons. Each successive dynode is more positive than the preceding one and electron multiplication takes place at each stage. This current multiplication is found to be linear over a very wide range. Indeed one of the virtues of photoelectric devices is the fact that the output signal is directly proportional to the incident light intensity. The multiplication is quite sensitive to applied dynode voltages and the high voltage power supply must be well regulated. We shall consider power supplies in some detail later in this section.

The 1P21 photomultiplier has nine stages and, when operated with 100 volts per stage, gives an average secondary emission yield of 4. The total multiplication for the nine stages is therefore 4^9 which is approximately 250,000. Thus for each photoelectron released at the cathode about a quarter of a million electrons are collected at the anode. This large current gain considerably simplifies the circuitry required to measure the photocurrent produced by a star. Even so, the anode current is quite small. At room temperature the dark current from an average 1P21 is about 2×10^{-9} amperes. Superimposed on this is a random fluctuation or noise current. The R.M.S. value of this dark noise is about 2×10^{-11} amperes and corresponds roughly to the emission of 100 electrons per second from the photocathode. This noise establishes the lower limit for a measurable signal. If the photomultiplier is refrigerated to dry ice temperatures ($-78°C$) the dark current and dark noise decrease by a factor of about 100. Some commercial photomultipliers exist with dark noise of this order at room temperature but are relatively expensive.

For operation of a photomultiplier at room temperature an amplifier capable of full scale output for an input current of 10^{-9} amperes (1 millimicroamp) is satisfactory. DC amplifiers of this type are usually operated with a voltage gain of unity and a current gain of the order of one million. It is important that the amplifier be linear and have high gain stability. This is usually accomplished by employing large negative feedback. In order to understand these amplifiers better let us first consider the principle of feedback illustrated in Figure 2–11. If a voltage e is applied to the input terminals 1 and 2 of this amplifier a voltage appears across the output terminals 3 and 4 of amplitude Ae; this is the output voltage:

$$E_o = Ae \tag{1}$$

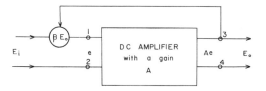

Figure 2–11.

Now if a fraction of the output voltage βE_o is fed back to the input then the voltage e is the sum of the applied input voltage E_i and the feedback voltage, that is,

$$e = E_i + \beta E_o = E_i + \beta A e_o \qquad (2)$$

or

$$E_i = e - \beta A e \qquad (3)$$

Now the voltage gain G of the amplifier with feedback is given by the ratio of output to input voltage,

$$G = \frac{E_o}{E_i} \qquad (4)$$

and on substituting equations (1) and (3) into (4) we find that

$$G = \frac{Ae}{e - \beta A e} = \frac{A}{1 - \beta A} \qquad (5)$$

If the voltage gain A is sufficiently large so that βA is much greater than unity then the feedback gain becomes essentially $-1/\beta$. If the feedback voltage is of opposite polarity to the input then the feedback is called negative feedback and β is a negative number. Further if all the output voltage is fed back to the input then the amplifier is said to have 100 percent negative feedback and $\beta = -1$. In this case,

$$G = \frac{A}{1 + A} \qquad (6)$$

and for large values of A the gain is unity. The important feature of such an amplifier is that changes in amplifier characteristics, tube aging, etc., do not significantly effect the over-all gain. The gain is still unity to one part in a thousand whether the amplifier gain without feedback (open loop gain) is 1,000 or 10,000.

Now consider an amplifier designed to give full-scale deflection on a 1 milliamp meter when a 10^{-9} ampere input current is applied. Such an amplifier is shown schematically in Figure 2–12.

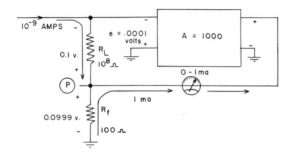

Figure 2–12.

A large input resistor R_L of 100 Megohms ($10^8 \Omega$) is used to develop a voltage drop of 0.1 volts from the photomultiplier current of 10^{-9} amperes. This current also flows through the feedback resistor R_f to ground but since its value is only 100 ohms the voltage drop is insignificant. The output voltage of the amplifier is developed across R_f and is equal to the input voltage to within one-part-in-a-thousand as shown from equation (6). The difference between the input voltage and the feedback or output voltage appears across the input terminals as a voltage of .0001 volts, which when amplified yields the 0.0999 volt output. That is, as long as the open loop gain A remains large, point P will always be driven to very nearly equal the input voltage. Now since R_f was chosen to be 100 and the voltage drop across it is essentially 0.1 volts, then the current flowing through the feedback resistor and the meter must be 1 milliampere. If the input current were 10^{-8} amperes we could produce a full-scale deflection by either reducing R_L to 10^7

ohms or increasing R_f to 1000 ohms. Usually fine sensitivity changes are made by changing R_f and coarse decade steps by changing R_L. This then is the principal employed in most simple DC amplifiers.

Since a DC amplifier is direct coupled any change in supply voltage or in tube characteristics is indistinguishable from an applied signal and therefore results in a zero drift. This zero drift may be minimized by proper circuit design and by the use of well regulated power supplies. The voltage regulator operates on a principal similar to that already discussed, namely the use of feedback. Figure 2–13 indicates the basic elements of a voltage regulator.

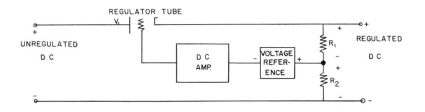

Figure 2–13.

The unregulated DC voltage is regulated by means of the variation in plate resistance of the regulator tube V_1. If the regulated output voltage were to increase it could be returned to the operating value by making the grid of V_1 more negative hence increasing its resistance. This is accomplished by tapping off a fraction of the output voltage dropped across R_2 and comparing it with a standard voltage reference source. This voltage reference could be a voltage regulator tube or a stable battery. If the voltage across R_2 becomes larger than the reference voltage, a positive voltage appears in the input of the DC amplifier which drives the regulator tube grid more negative. If the voltage across R_2 is less than the reference voltage a negative voltage appears at the amplifier input resulting in a decrease in the plate resistance of V_1. Thus if the gain of the DC amplifier is sufficiently high the voltage across R_2 will be held as constant as the voltage reference source, and hence the larger regulated DC output will remain as steady as the reference voltage. Regulators of this type may be used for both the DC amplifier power supply and the photomultiplier dynode supply. A completely adequate and economical high voltage dynode supply may be provided by batteries, however.

The DC amplifier circuit shown in Figure 2–14 has been used by many astronomers with considerable success. The circuit was first described by Valley and Wallman in M.I.T. Radiation Laboratory Series Volume 18 and is usually referred to as the M.I.T. amplifier. In this schematic diagram the dynode voltages are supplied by a battery box consisting of three U200, 300 volt batteries in series. The positive side is grounded and a coaxial connector is used to feed the photomultiplier. The 10K series resistor protects the batteries from an external short and incidentally provides protection for the experimenter as well. The batteries should be adequately insulated to prevent leakage paths to ground and should also be shielded. A wooden box which has aluminium foil cemented to the inside and is covered by wax paper or other suitable insulating material provides a satisfactory battery container. The connector shell should make contact with the aluminium shielding. The connection between the battery box and photomultiplier should be a shielded coaxial cable, the shielding being at ground potential on the positive side of the batteries.

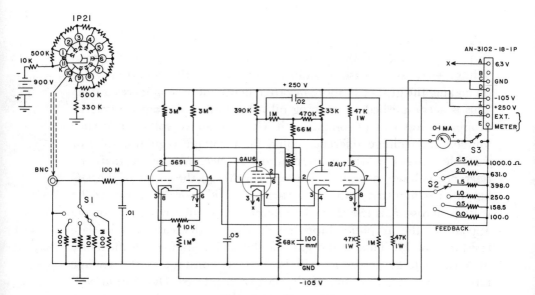

Figure 2–14. DC Amplifier.

The individual dynode voltages are provided by the series resistor voltage divider. The voltage between the last dynode and ground is smaller than the interstage voltages. These divider resistors may be soldered directly to the tube socket pins. It is very important that the photomultiplier base and socket be clean and dry to avoid large leakage currents. To keep the circuitry clean do not use solder flux in making solder joints in the photomultiplier housing or in the first stage of the amplifier. The wired tube socket and base may be cleaned with isopropyl alcohol. The anode connection, pin 10, should be brought out separately, preferably with a shielded wire to a separate low leakage connector such as a BNC. The shielded cable from the anode connector to the amplifier input should be kept as short as possible and free from flexure. Except for special coaxial cable a small transient signal is developed by flexing the cable.

Care should be exercised in wiring the amplifier input circuit to avoid leakage to the ground. The coarse gain switch S1 should preferably be a ceramic switch. The photomultiplier current develops an input signal across one of the input load resistors. The brightest stars would be observed with the 100K resistor. The steps increase in decades, each step corresponding to $2\frac{1}{2}$ magnitudes increase in sensitivity. These resistors are one percent deposited carbon resistors. The series 100 Megohm resistor and the 0.01 μ *farad* capacitor provide a 1 second time constant for all gains but the highest where the time constant is 2 seconds. The introduction of these time constants smooths out the rapid fluctuations.

The first stage of the amplifier is a pair of balanced triodes to reduce drift produced by changes in power supply voltage and tube aging. To minimize the effects of heater supply variations a twin triode should be used. The type 5691 tube is a twin triode high performance version of a 6SL7. The feedback is applied to the second triode section of this tube and the operation of the amplifier is to always drive this second grid to the same potential as the input grid. The amplifier is balanced by the 10K potentiometer in the cathode circuit. This zero adjustment is usually a ten turn precision potentiometer. The other resistors in the input stage are 1 per cent deposited carbon resistors. The signals at the plates of the 5691 are coupled directly to the grid of the 6AU6 pentode and one half of the 12AU7 triode. This avoids the zero drift that would be present if a voltage divider were used. The bias for enabling these tubes to couple directly to the 5691 plates is provided by the common

60K cathode resistor. The output of the 6AU6 is fed to a cathode follower through a voltage divider. With zero input signal and proper balance by the 10K potentiometer the cathode of the cathode follower should be at ground potential. The output current flows through one of the six feedback resistors which are connected to the second grid of the input tube to provide 100 per cent negative feedback. The voltage across the feedback resistor is almost identical to that developed across the input load resistor and the analysis follows that of Figure 2–11, discussed earlier. The fine sensitivity switch S2 varies the gain in steps of $\frac{1}{2}$ magnitudes. When the 100 ohm feedback resistor is in, 0.1 volts at the input produces full scale deflection on the 1 milliamp meter, while 1 volt produces full scale deflection in 1000 ohm position. These feedback resistors are usually wire wound; however ordinary carbon resistors with values close to the desired resistance may be purchased and filed to bring them to the proper value for $\frac{1}{2}$ magnitude steps. It is necessary to have a wheatstone bridge available if you are to make these resistors yourself. It is not necessary, of course, to have steps of $\frac{1}{2}$ magnitude and any convenient range provided by commercial 1 per cent resistors may be used. Leads are brought out to connectors to provide for an external meter or chart recorder in series with the amplifier meter. When the external meter is not in use the switch S3 shorts across this connector.

To test the stability and noise of this amplifier a small resistor of the order of 10 ohms may be shunted across the feedback resistor. A 10-ohm resistor would give a voltage sensitivity of 10 millivolts for full scale deflection. You can expect to see noise of the order of 1 millivolt and drift rates of the order of 1 millivolt per hour. By selecting and/or aging the input tube for two or three days this may be improved.

Figure 2–15 shows a power supply suitable for providing the $+250$ volts and -105 volts for the DC amplifier. It is best if the power supply is built on a separate chassis. In fact, the amplifier itself may be made compact enough to mount directly on the telescope. The -105 volt supply is obtained from a VR 105 voltage regulator tube. The $+250$ volt supply uses a vacuum tube regulator. The 6L6 is controlled by the DC amplifier utilizing a 6SL7 twin triode. The output voltage is referenced to a 5651 VR tube which runs at 87 volts. The regulation of this power supply should be better than 0.1 percent over a range of AC line variations from 100 volts to 130 volts.

It is convenient to have a high voltage power supply capable of a

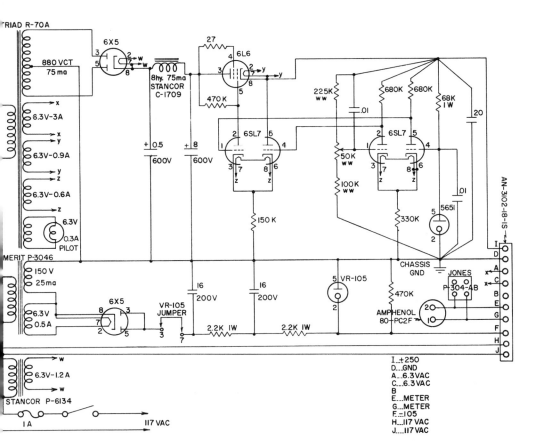

Figure 2–15. Regulated power supply.

variable output providing from, say, 75 volts per stage to 120 volts per stage to the photomultiplier. It is then possible to select the voltage that provides the optimum signal to noise ratio. This may be done by the use of batteries and a switch to tap off at different voltages. A rather compact battery box can be made using Y20S, 30 volt batteries.

Figure 2–16 shows an electronic high voltage supply. The voltage is generated by an R.f. oscillator operating at about 100 kc. This voltage is rectified and a small fraction is tapped off to a voltage regulator whose output controls the amplitude of the oscillator voltage. By varying the voltage tapped off the total voltage is changed. The virtue of the R.f. source is that it makes a much lighter unit and is not nearly as dangerous as the 1,000 volts obtained from 110 volt 60 cycle line.

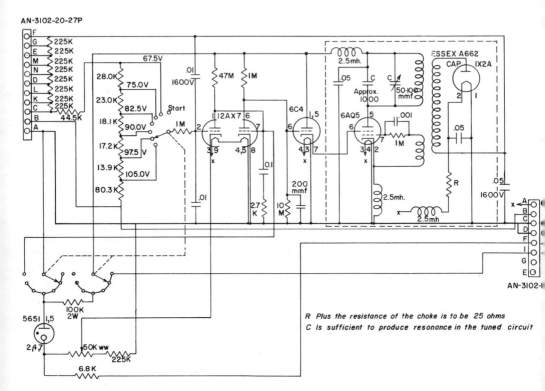

Figure 2–16. High-voltage power supply.

The amplifier and power supply described above are capable of providing stable measurements accurate to a few tenths of a percent. Obviously, a simple 0–1 ma panel meter is not sufficient to read the output to better than a few per cent. The simplest recording device would be a large scale 0–1 ma meter preferably with a mirror scale to avoid parallax. A meter such as a Weston 901 would be quite satisfactory but an observing assistant would then prove very valuable, and an objective technique for reading the meter deflections must be set up. Usually the meter readings are recorded at, say, 15-second intervals and the meter read at its position at that second. Clearly a continuous record of the photometer output would be more desirable. If a paper chart recorder is used a single observer can work efficiently with a constant record of his work timed by the chart drive and requiring only an occasional note or time mark to be written on the chart recorder.

Recorders such as a Leeds and Northrup Speedomax or a Minneapolis-Honeywell-Brown recorder cost about $1,000. However, there are a number of less expensive chart recorders on the market such as the Rustrak or Varian that may be within the budget of an enthusiastic amateur.

There are today numerous DC amplifiers and high voltage power supplies on the market that the amateur might consider purchasing. Indeed, it is difficult to buy the components to construct the electronics yourself for much less than the cost of these commercial units. By far the best bargains in electronics are those provided by kit manufacturers. A vacuum tube voltmeter is a DC amplifier and may be purchased in kit form for as low as $30. None of these vacuum tube voltmeters is suitable for use as a photometer but may be modified to provide an amplifier of moderate capability. Most kit VTVM's, such as Heathkit, Eico, and RCA Voltomist Jr., have a 10-Megohm input impedance and the lowest voltage sensitivity is the order of 3 volts.

This means that a current of 3×10^{-7} amperes will produce a full-scale deflection. A study of the circuit will reveal how these gains may be increased. Several of the meters will work if the 10-Megohm input resistor is replaced by a 100-Megohm resistor. The meter scales are large enough to be read accurately and with a little ingenuity a workable amplifier can be built from a VTVM. This at least would provide a start and with time a better amplifier could be built or purchased.

The DC amplifiers made by companies such as General Radio, Kiethly, and Kintel have been adapted by professional astronomers to photometery and should be investigated by the amateur. Many companies make excellent and relatively inexpensive high voltage power supplies.

Having discussed this instrumentation at some length in the preceding pages it is well to point out the role of the observer. No amount of instrumental sophistication is going to unlock the secrets of the universe; only skill and imagination will produce significant results. Remember, in spite of your equipment, the observing technique is the trick.

CHAPTER 3

Multicolor Observations

BY GERALD E. KRON

Lick Observatory, University of California
Mt. Hamilton, California

INTRODUCTION

Many of us can remember from our childhoods the thrill of finding colored bits of glass in odd places such as in the remains of bonfires or in small scale rubbish dumps. Such colored glass usually came from broken bottles which may have contained various kinds of patent medicine. The vendors of these nostrums may have adopted a colored glass bottle to strain out certain harmful elements of light and in this way prolong the life of their product. On the other hand they may have simply been trying to exploit the human tendency to be attracted by bright pretty colors, the very thing that led most of us as children to pick up the broken bit and carry it home. A more serious use for bits of colored glass has been for decorative art, especially for making the windows of churches and cathedrals, an art form that has been practiced for many centuries. Many, many years ago, the pellucid beauty of stained glass windows must have been an important factor in stimulating the development of methods of coloring glass in every possible shade and hue, making available to artists past and present a material so durable as to resist indefinitely even the action of direct sunlight. The reason for mentioning all this here is that the availability of these colored glasses has a considerable bearing on the success of certain observational techniques of modern astronomy, for out of colored glass can be made the best broadband absorption filters for the measurement of the colors of stars and other luminous components of our universe.

In order better to understand the role of color measurement, or multiplecolor photometry, it may be appropriate to start by mentioning the hackneyed point that most of what we know about the world external to the little bit on which we live has been learned by a slow and meticulous working over of knowledge gained only from the light

79

we receive, light that in spite of the power of our largest telescopes is sometimes received at a rate of only a few quanta per second. From this light we must extract the maximum amount of information. From that information we formulate our theories about the past, the present, and the future of our universe. It is the duty of observers to extract the information, a duty much hindered by effects of the earth's atmosphere. This atmosphere, though it sustains our lives, deprives us of nearly all the ultraviolet light radiated by the objects of our interest, and much of the infrared. There is left to us in that part of the electromagnetic spectrum called light the well known region extending from about 3,100Å. to about 12,000Å., little less than four octaves. Shortward of 3,100Å complete opacity is caused by molecules of ozone, O_3, in the upper atmosphere. Longward of 12,000Å there is serious absorption from water vapor and carbon dioxide molecules, though there are a few "windows" shortward of 40,000Å which have been used by some observers. Fortunately the part of the spectrum available to earth-bound observers is interesting and valuable, whereas much of the unavailable part, especially in the infrared, is less important as far as we know.

What can we learn from this light? An obvious and very important thing to investigate is the intensity distribution of the light with wavelength. Spread it out into a spectrum. That is, systematically sort out the wavelengths in order of size and then measure the intensity within each increment of wavelength. But how small should the increments of wavelength be? A hundred Angstrom units? Ten? One? The tool seems to get sharper as the wavelength interval is made less and less, until finally we should be able to learn everything—but there is danger of learning everything about nothing! For if this process is reduced to absurdity and the wavelength interval is reduced to zero, then obviously there will be no light at all to measure within a single interval. Now we can simply gather at one extreme all available light and measure its intensity thus learning this one and only fact. At the other extreme we can divide it into wavelengths so fine that the intensity is so small in each wavelength unit as to be immeasurable without spending an impracticable amount of time waiting for quanta to be collected. Little or nothing is learned by making measurements according to either of these extreme methods. If we subdivide the available wavelength region into many subdivisions of measurable size we practice spectrophotometry and can learn very much about the light provided it is bright enough. If the light source is too faint for spectrophotometry we can divide the spectrum into a few coarse subdivisions each of which contains a fairly large fraction of the total available light. This latter technique is called *wideband, multicolor photometry.* Available published magnitudes and "colors" all result from this commonly used method. It is convenient and easy to apply and the results are so useful and informative, that it is used for photometry of very faint objects and for bright ones as well. This chapter will deal principally with photoelectric wideband multicolor photometry.

COLOR PROPERTIES OF PHOTOCATHODES

Nowadays nearly all photoelectric measurements are made with just a few types of photoemissive cathode surfaces. These surfaces are usually built into multiplier phototubes. In fact the technique of employing simple diode photocells is difficult enough to discourage most persons in the field and so the multiplier principle now is supreme in photoelectric work. In the practice of multicolor photometry the color characteristics of the photocathode are of prime importance, so important in fact that the color properties of the photocathode may have as much or more to do with the design of a multicolor system than the properties of starlight. Let us look at some of the color properties of photocathodes now in use. The most important cathode material in use by astronomers is without doubt the opaque antimony-cesium so-called alloy surface. The well known RCA type 1P21 has a cathode of this type, referred to as an S4 surface by its manufacturers. The spectral sensitivity of this kind of surface to light of uniform distribution of brightness with wavelength is illustrated in figure 3–1 where the curve was taken from the RCA Tube Manual. A new cathode type is the tri-alkali surface, highly sensitive in an absolute sense and with unusually high sensitivity to red light which is light between 6,000 to 7,000A°. A sensitivity curve for this type of cathode, called the S20, also from RCA, is given in Figure 3-1. The tri-alkali surface so far has not been much used for astronomical photometry, but it is mentioned here because it seems destined for such extensive use that it may even replace the S4 surface. The third type of cathode important in astronomy is the cesium-oxide-on-silver surface or the S1. Strictly speaking the S1 surface is an opaque version, where all multipliers with this kind of cathode response are of the transparent kind. Therefore the curve given for this surface in Figure 3-1 is taken from measurements made by Joel Stebbins and me on our six-color multiplier called L2 furnished to us by Professor A. Lallemand of the Paris Observatory. Obviously the output from multipliers with these three cathode surfaces used without filters would give different information if exposed to starlight. Conversely, if their properties were to be modified by means of color filters so that all would yield equivalent information then identical filters could not be used with all of them. The filters would have to be tailored to fit the cathode characteristic and the color system desired by the observer. It is interesting to compare the sensitivity distribution of the classic potassium hydride photosurface used by most photoelectric observers until about 1938 with the modern types and also with the sensitivity distribution of the human eye. Both of these are also given in Figure 3-1. The superiority of the more modern photosurfaces with respect to width of spectral response and their correspondingly greater usefulness for multicolor photometry is evident from the figure.

When a photocathode is employed for colorimetry it is important to understand that the color sensitivity of photocathodes is dependent upon their temperature. When a multiplier with a semitransparent Sb-Cs cathode is cooled from room temperature to the temperature of dry ice (from $+20°C$ to $-79°C$, a range of practically $100°C$), relatively speaking, the cathode surface becomes more sensitive to blue light (or less sensitive to yellow light). If the multiplier is in use with blue and yellow filters of the kinds commonly used for astronomical photometry, the change will amount to about 0.15 magnitude or more. Therefore it is important to insure that no large temperature changes will take place in the cathode of a multiplier being used for precise colorimetry.

FILTERS AND SOME GENERAL PROPERTIES

We now come to the important subject of filters to be used with the photosensitive surfaces briefly described above for making useful multicolor photometric observations. Either glass or dyed gelatin filters may

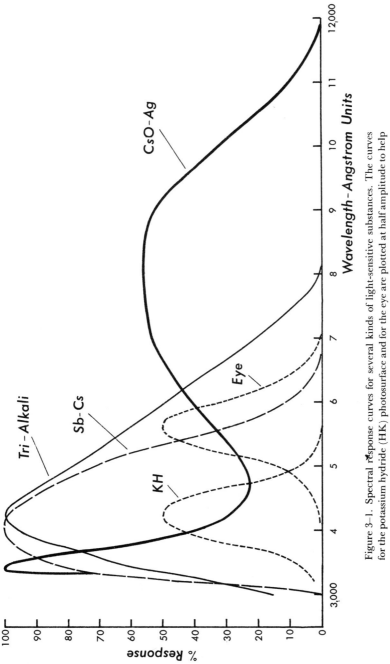

Figure 3–1. Spectral response curves for several kinds of light-sensitive substances. The curves for the potassium hydride (HK) photosurface and for the eye are plotted at half amplitude to help reduce confusion. Relative ordinates for the various devices are arbitrary.

be used for astronomical purposes. Though dyed gelatin is often criticised as being unstable the criticism is generally not valid if the gelatin is cemented between pieces of glass and is kept out of strong light. However glass filters are available that will do practically every-thing that gelatin ones will do. As these are above criticism it is better to use them whenever possible. Gelatin filters are useful if the thickness of a complex combination filter gets too large. Then sometimes thickness can be reduced by cementing one gelatin filter between two glass ones. In addition there are some infrared transmitting gelatin filters that are better than available glass filters. Gelatin filter stock is avai-able from the Eastman Kodak Co., Rochester, New York. Glass filters are available from several manufacturers, but the Corning Glass Co. and the Schott Co. make enough between them for most astronomical purposes. The Corning Glass Co. control their filter characteristics by grinding the blanks until a thickness is reached which yields the catalogue characteristic required. Hence thickness in millimeters of Corning filters has little meaning. The Schott Co., on the other hand controls the melt, and their catalogue transmission curves are for filter stock having a given thickness in mm. Changing the thickness of a filter obviously will affect the transmission of a filter at a given wave-length, in the sense that a thinner piece will transmit more light than a thick one. The relative transmission goes as an exponential function of the relative thickness. For example, if we have two pieces of filter stock, A and B, which have transmissions of T_a and T_b at a given wavelength, then the transmission of both of them together is $T_a \times T_b$. If both transmit 50 per cent, then the total transmission will be 0.50×0.50 or 0.25, equivalent to 25 per cent. Thus doubling the thickness of a given filter will reduce the transmission at any given wavelength by an amount obtained by squaring the transmission. In general if T_a and T_b are the transmissions of similar filter stock of thicknesses t_a and t_b

$$T_a = T_b^{(t_b/t_a)}$$

There are two precautions to keep in mind. First, no filter can have a maximum transmission at any wavelength greater than that deter-mined by the reflection losses at its surface, which in turn depend upon the index of refraction of the glass and the wavelength of the light. To a good approximation, this loss can be taken as $4\frac{1}{2}$ per cent per surface, which can be reduced by coating the surfaces of the filter with a nonreflecting layer. Second, filters much reduced in thickness may have transmission bands appear in surprising wavelength regions, not to be anticipated from an examination of the transmission curves given in the catalogues. This is because some colored glasses have feeble transmission bands of such small percentage that they lie hidden because of the coarse transmission scale used in the catalogues. However, when the glass is made thin these bands can become prominent and the whole character of the transmission of the glass can change. The Schott catalogue lists the transmission of their filter glasses uncorrected for the surface reflection losses; the Corning catalogue shows the actual transmission of each piece of glass, reflection loss included. This is why some of the Schott glasses have in some catalogued spectral regions, transmissions as large as 99 per cent, while the maximum catalogued transmission of any Corning filter is usually about 91 per cent.

PROPERTIES OF SOME SPECIFIC FILTERS

Generally there are two types of color filters, band-pass filters and "low-pass" filters, where the "low" refers to the frequency of light, not the wavelength. Usually, low-pass filters have superior characteristics to band-pass filters. For some reason the glass in low-pass filters usually takes a good polish, is reasonably free from striae, and the coloring material gives more sharp and definite "cuts" than band-pass filters. The low-pass filters are the yellows and the reds; they reject the shorter wavelengths. Glass low-pass filters are excellent for cuts from about 3,000Å to about 7,000Å, though one useful Corning filter (7-56, made from Corning 2540 glass) has a good cut at about 8,500Å. Generally the best variety of sharp cut red and infrared transmitting filters that cut longward of 6,500Å are the dyed gelatin filters. As a rule the Schott yellow and red filters are superior optically to the Corning, and, in addition, they are thinner. The band pass filters are the ultraviolet, blue, and green filters. Of these, the most difficult to deal with are the ultraviolet filters, partly because all UV filters leak red and infrared light, and partly because the glass is nearly opaque to visible light and usually full of defects. The best UV filter is Schott UG 2. This glass comes with a good surface polish and has high maximum transmission in just the right spectral region for an ultraviolet color.

The red leak is relatively small, especially if the glass is used in a 2-mm thickness instead of the catalogued 1-mm thickness. The main trouble with this glass is that it tends to have included bubbles. Each piece should be examined by looking through the filter stock at the glowing filament of an unfrosted light bulb. If the filter stock is moved around in front of the filament, its entire area can be surveyed, and the filter can be cut from the best area. Direct sunlight can also be seen through this filter stock, so the sun can be used for a bubble survey. Another commonly used UV filter stock is Corning 7-54, made from Corning 9863 glass. The principle advantage of this glass is its high transmission in the desired spectral region. Disadvantages are its high leakage in the red, starting at 6,600Å catalogue value but uncontrolled by the manufacturers, and its tendency to have striae and a defective surface quality evidently caused by the effects of nonuniform hardness. This is a very soft glass, easy to grind, and quick to take a polish. The transmission of this glass in standard thickness is shown in Figure 3-2; the red leakage is very evident. A very useful violet filter is Schott BG 12 which isolates a nice transmission band centered at about 4,100Å, and even in 1 mm thickness has remarkably small infrared leakage and no red leakage. Corning 5-61 is a filter of this type (made from 5562 glass) and is also very good but is thicker than the Schott glass. One of the best blue filters is Corning 5-56 (5031 glass) which has a transmission band centered at about 4,400Å and a red leak that does not start until almost 7,200Å. Schott does not make as good a blue glass as this Corning product. It is unfortunate that 5-56 is usually badly affected by prominent striae and the part of a blank from which a filter is to be cut must be carefully selected. The best green filter is Schott BG 18. This filter leaks no appreciable infrared until 16,000Å in 2-mm thickness. It has a long transmission tail shortward to 3,250Å but this can be cut off by combining the BG18 with the yellow filters GG5 or GG11 to give a clean band pass in the green. Corning has a filter of this sort called 4-96 but it is usually very thick and so badly affected with striae that perfect areas are almost impossible to find. The transmission of BG18 is shown in Figure 3-2. One more kind of filter remains to be mentioned. If one wishes to measure an ultraviolet magnitude with the S1 photocathode the infrared leak of even the UG2 glass will interfere seriously and at best must be measured and corrected. At worst the leak may be so large on the light of a red star that almost no precision is left after a correction. What is needed is an additional filter element to "plug" the leak. The only common material known that will do this is an aqueous solution of pure copper sulfate. The copper sulfate must be chemically pure because a common impurity of technical copper sulfate is iron sulfate which will much reduce the ultraviolet transparency of the copper sulfate. Prepare an 80 per cent saturated solution by letting an excess of $CuSO_4$ stand in distilled water for a day or more at room temperature. Pour off the solution; then add to it 20 per cent more distilled water. Use this for a filling between two 1-mm thick pieces of UG2 held about an $\frac{1}{8}$ of an inch apart by a rubber "0" ring; a ring of pure metallic copper like a finger ring but much thinner included just inside the "0" ring seems to prolong the life of the filter. The filter should be renewed about every two weeks as its transmission slowly decreases. The infrared leak when used with an S1 cathode multiplier is only about 0.1 per cent of the deflection through an infrared filter made on Corning 7-56. There is almost always a small bubble in a liquid filled filter. This bubble will always be at one edge and is harmless if so small that it does not cut the light beam. The bubble may be seen by illuminating the filter from the sun or from the glowing filament of an unfrosted light bulb.

Filter glass can be obtained from the manufacturers in squares 2, 3, or 6 inches on a side with even larger pieces available on special order. The cost is considerable; 2-inch squares polished to specified thickness cost from $4.00 to $8.00 each depending upon the type of glass, whereas molded unpolished 6-inch squares in full thickness (4 to 8 mm) cost from $6.00 each to over $20.00. Filters for astronomical use can be cut from the square stock with a cookie cutter and some No. 180 carborundum. If the filters are made $\frac{3}{4}$ inch in diameter four of them can be cut from a perfect 2-inch square blank. The blank should be fastened to a piece of window glass with a stiff wax such as "half-and-half" (half beeswax and half rosin). Cutting should be slow to avoid overheating, and the cutter should be allowed to penetrate about 1 mm into the backing glass. Otherwise the filter will have a feather edge. Be careful not to handle the finished filter much with carborundum-charged hands as some of the filter glasses scratch much more easily than more common glasses. This precaution makes removal of a feather edge by hand grinding somewhat difficult.

A most useful stock is Corning 9-54 made from 7910 glass, also known as "Vicor." This material is 96 per cent silica and will transmit all of the astronomical ultraviolet. It is an excellent substitute for clear fused quartz for field lenses, UV filter covers, windows to multiplier holders, etc.

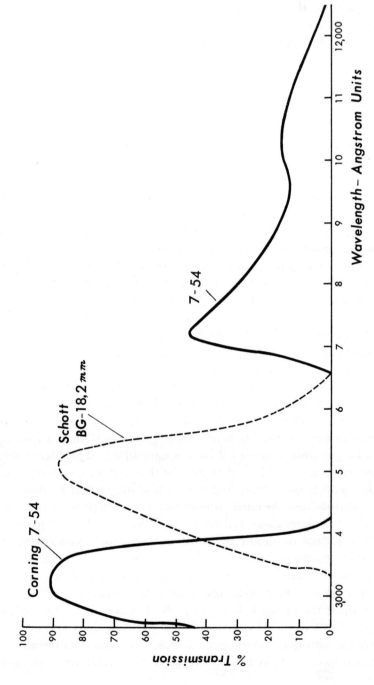

Figure 3–2. Transmission curves of two representative kinds of glass filters.

COLOR SYSTEMS

Any observer can create at will a perfectly good "color system" with a telescope, a photoelectric photometer, and some pieces of colored glass. Figure 3-1 shows that the 1P21 with its Sb-Cs cathode has a rather broad spectral response, especially when compared with the eye or with the old KH photocell. It is possible with appropriate filters, to carve the response of the 1P21 into three parts useful for a three color system. Some observers have constructed a four color system around the 1P21, but the gain in the number of colors has been about compensated by the loss in response owing to the narrow filter bands and in base line caused by squeezing the color regions closer together. In considering the merits of any color system it should be remembered that the spacing of the color regions should go as the reciprocal of the wavelength in order to preserve the ability of the color differences to resolve such effects on the color of starlight as the temperature of the star or the degree of space reddening that affects the starlight. Therefore little is gained in adding a red color to an existing, say, ultraviolet-blue-yellow color system, unless the red color is well out at around 8,000Å. Even the tri-alkali cathode color characteristics do not permit the establishment of a really good fourth color in the red, although it is superior in this respect to the 1P21 cathode.

In deciding on a multiple color system there is always some advantage in adhering, if possible, to some standard system that has already been used extensively by someone else; then all of the other observers' results are available to compare with your own. For this reason the rest of this discussion on color systems will be limited to a description of the properties of three photoelectric systems that have been extensively employed; the UBV system of three color photometry in the ultraviolet, blue, and visual spectral regions; the PVI photometry in the photographic, visual, and infrared regions; and the six-color photometry in six spectral regions, u, v, b, g, r, and i meaning ultra, violet, blue, green, red, and infra.

Of these the easiest to use is the UBV system as it was designed for use with the 1P21 and other multipliers having the Sb-Cs (S4) photocathode. The three spectral regions are best isolated with 2 mm of UG2 for the ultraviolet, 2 mm of GG13 + 1 mm of BG12 for the blue, and 2 mm of GG14 for the yellow, or "visual." The GG13, which looks like clear glass, restricts the transmission of the BG12 at its shortward edge so that there is no sensitivity within the region of continuous absorption by hydrogen in stellar atmospheres, that is, no sensitivity within the "balmer continuum." This precaution makes possible linear transformations between color differences on the photoelectric systems of different observers. If these filters are placed inside of the focus of the telescope, their different thicknesses will affect the focal point. Thus, if the observer wishes to observe through the smallest possible aperture, the thicknesses of the ultraviolet and yellow filters must be built up to equal optically that of the thickest of the three filters, the B filter. This is, of course, a general principle applicable to all filters. The UBV system can be used only with telescopes that transmit ultraviolet light. This system has been used extensively for attacking problems in interstellar absorption, stellar classification, properties of stars in clusters, and problems in stellar evolution.

Another three color system is the so-called "PVI" system, where the initials mean "photographic," "visual," and "infrared." The first two colors are close imitations of the International photographic and photovisual colors. The I color is an infrared system that has already been standardized and on which published magnitudes are available, but it has been added to the P and V to form a useful three color system that can be used with a refracting telescope because no ultraviolet color is included. If all three colors are to be measured with one instrument at one time a multiplier with a CsO-Ag (S1) photocathode, such as the RCA 7102, must be used (Figure 3-1). The filters are P, 2 mm of BG23 plus 1 mm of BG12 plus 2 mm of WG1 cemented with balsam and outer surfaces with nonreflecting coatings of cryolite, if possible (the BG23 and the WG1 are on the outside of the sandwich). The V filter is 2 mm of GG11 plus 2 mm of BG18 cemented with balsam. The infra filter is Wratten 89 gelatin cemented with balsam between glass and Corning 1-59 (3966 glass). The S1 cathodes differ somewhat one from another and if the photometer deflections through the three filters are unbalanced badly the infra filter may be changed. For example if more infra response is needed, the Corning 1-59 could be thinned or a gelatin that cuts at a shorter wavelength could be substituted for the W89. The S1 photoelectric surface is only about 1/40 as sensitive as the Sb-Cs surface so if greater sensitivity is needed, the P and V colors may be measured with the B and V filters and a 1P21, while the I can be measured separately with the S1 multiplier and the infra filter mentioned earlier in this paragraph or with a more transparent filter consisting of 2 mm of RG2 glass. This method works well but the references to standard stars must be done with more than average care.

Probably the most powerful broad band multiple color photometry is the six-color photometry. This photometry can be done only with a multiplier having the CsO-Ag (S1) surface. Because of the broad spectral range, from an effective (u) wavelength of about 3,600Å to about (i) 10,000Å, and the differences that exist among the S1 cathodes, it is usually necessary to experiment with filters in order to balance them nicely. It is quite possible to modify the filters by selecting materials and thicknesses so that the v, b, g, and r deflections are of nearly the same size on light of stars of spectral type about F5. The u and i deflections are usually smaller in size but this is tolerable. Figure 3–3 shows the spectral regions of the six-color photometer in use at the Lick Observatory employing a Lallemand 12-stage multiplier with a CsO-Ag cathode and filters to be described presently. Figure 3–3 differs from both Figure 3–1 and Figure 3–2 in that it portrays the combined characteristics of the multiplier and the filters, and it may be useful to describe how the data were obtained. A laboratory-type quartz prism spectrometer was set up with the entrance slit illuminated with light from a ribbon filament tungsten lamp. Then the intensity of the output was measured with a vacuum thermopile as a function of wavelength as the wavelength control was used to scan the spectrum. The photometer with its filters then was substituted for the thermopile and the range of each filter transmission was scanned with the spectrometer, response data now being taken from the photometer. The thermopile calibration now was employed to transform the photometer response from what was measured at the output of the spectrometer to what would have been measured if the output light from the spectrometer had been of uniform intensity with wavelength. These data, reduced further to equal maxima for each filter simply for tidiness, are then plotted in Figure 3–3. The short vertical lines show how the effective wavelength for each filter varies with the color of the star light from very blue stars to very red stars.

The six-color photometry must be done with a multiplier with an S1 surface, a multiplier type that cannot be used successfully for astronomical colorimetry unless it is refrigerated with dry ice or with liquid air. Furthermore, it is advisable if possible to select the multiplier

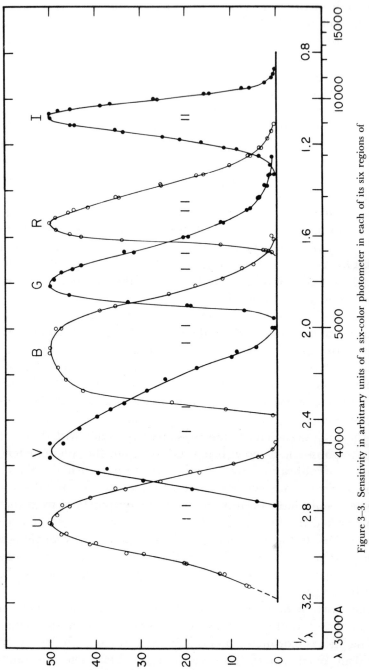

Figure 3–3. Sensitivity in arbitrary units of a six-color photometer in each of its six regions of spectral sensitivity. The short vertical lines indicate effective wavelengths to (left) the light of very blue stars and (right) the light of very red stars.

for cathode sensitivity extending as far into the infrared as possible, to 12,000Å for example. To make matters worse the filters cannot be made according to cookbook practice, but must be "trimmed" to give reasonably balanced deflections from a given multiplier; thus a given filter set goes with a given multiplier. It is clear from all of this that the six-color photometry represents a rather sophisticated experimental approach to colorimetry and anyone who wishes to try it should be well provided with time, patience, and money. The best multiplier easily available is the RCA 7102 at a cost of $110 each, provided the multiplier is selected for high signal-to-noise ratio when refrigerated. The best multiplier to be used as a single sample from stock is probably the DuMont type K1613, a multiplier having an external structure, basing, and cost all the same as the 7102. A buyer who wishes the best results from a single purchase probably would do best with the DuMont cell though selection for infrared sensitivity would then have to be abandoned.

The six-color filters are as follows:

ultraviolet: 2 mm UG 2 + 2 mm 80 % $CuSo_4$ solution (this filter should be used as specified, the remaining five may be "trimmed")

violet: 2mm GG13 + 2mm BG19 + 3mm BG12, cemented with balsam

blue: 2mm GG5 + Corning 4303

green: 2mm OG1 + 2mm BG18 cemented with balsam

red: 2mm RG5 + Corning 3965 cemented with balsam

infrared: Corning 2540.

After filters like those described are made, it will be necessary to modify them by altering thicknesses or even glass types to eliminate unusually small or unusually large responses through any one filter, a process that is best left to the judgment and resourcefulness of the experimenter.

COLOR STANDARDS

During the course of a series of colorimetric observations, which may continue for years, many factors influence the stability of the instrumental color "system." The reflectivity of mirrors in the telescope will change with time; filters may change from deterioration of the surface polish; and the multiplier may change from temperature effects or from a necessity for changing the applied voltage. Furthermore a multiplier may become broken or may simply "go bad" with time and require substitution. Because of these instabilities inherent in the measuring equipment, all colorimetry must be stabilised by reference to objects having known, standard colors. Astronomers have picked stars for standard objects, usually fairly bright stars because they are easy to find and easy to measure. The procedure consists in observing a number of standard stars along with the "unknowns," then arbitrarily modifying the data so that the colors of the standard objects agree with their catalogued values. It is then assumed that the unknown objects have measurements on the same system. Five standard stars constitute a minimum, this is true only if the five stars have been carefully selected to have a good, long range in color. Ten standards are better arranged in two groups of about five, one group to be observed prior to the unknowns, the other to be observed after. The observer must decide for himself the economy involved; too few standards will result in observations having large systematic errors, too many in waste of observing time. Accuracy may be built up by repeating the observations. Repetition on one night helps little unless accuracy suffers from poor signal-to-noise ratio either from a noisy multiplier or measurements on faint objects. Accuracy is best improved by repeating the measurements on two or three nights, thus errors from imperfect extinction corrections are averaged. Of course measurements should not be made when the sky is known to be polluted with smoke, smog, or affected by cloud. An interesting fact is that the observer himself does not have to change his colors to the standard system. He can observe his unknowns along with the standards, and as long as the standards are adequate, the change from the instrumental system to the standard system can be done by anyone at any time.

Colors are usually expressed in terms of a color difference, that is, the difference in the brightness of the object as observed through each of two filters, expressed in magnitudes. A detailed description of the process of reduction is beyond the scope of this paper, but the following general description of the process may be appropriate. The data taken during observing are the photometer deflections through each filter on star and on sky (if the sky deflection is appreciable), and the hour angle of the object at the time of the observation. The net deflections on the object then are obtained by subtracting the sky deflection, the zenith distance is obtained from the declination of the object and its hour angle. From this zenith distance, and atmospheric extinction coefficients for each color valid at the observing site, one calculates what the deflections would have been if free from the absorbing effects of the terrestial atmosphere. The ratio of the deflections thus obtained may then be turned into magnitudes. Of course there are many variations of the way all of the steps may be done. Finally the instrumental color may be turned into the standard system, a process which is facilitated by a simple plot on graph paper; along one axis plot the standard colors of the standard stars, along the other, their instrumental colors; the graph so obtained may then be entered on the instrumental axis with the colors of the unknowns to find for each the standard color on the other axis.

A serious amateur astronomer who wishes to make contributions to colorimetry would do well to get the help of a professional in managing the reduction of his data. Professional help also should be sought in deciding on the selection of lists of colorimetric standards. Amateurs may be interested in examining some tabulations of standards however, so the following limited bibliography is given. References in these papers will give one a start into the literature. For the UBV system, H. L. Johnson and W. W. Morgan, *Astrophysical Journal*, 117: 313 (1953). For the PVI system, G. E. Kron and J. Lynn Smith, *Astrophysical Journal*, 113: 324 (1951), and G. E. Kron and N. U. Mayall, *Astronomical Journal*, 65, 581, 1960. For the six-color system, Joel Stebbins and G. E. Kron, *Astrophysical Journal*, 126: 266 (1957).

Astronomical colorimetry is interesting and rewarding work. It is easier, more straightforward, and capable of higher accuracy (expressed in magnitudes) than fundamental magnitude work because of the differential nature of the measurements. The applications are endless: the most superficial discussion of the uses of colorimetry would require more words than are in this whole chapter.

CHAPTER 4

Observing Techniques

BY FRANK M. BATESON

Royal Astronomical Society of New Zealand

The aim in discussing observing techniques in this chapter is to provide information that will be useful to the amateur observer. No attempt has been made to turn the amateur into a professional. While he may observe in order to aid in the accumulation of knowledge of the stars, the primary urge driving the amateur is his inborn love of the heavens and the deep personal satisfaction he derives from making useful observations. Thus the value of the amateur in the photoelectric field lies in securing accurate observations.

From the previous chapters, the observer will have realised that a photoelectric photometer is no longer an instrument for use solely by highly trained techicians. It is important to stress, however, that the apparatus described is not a toy. It should only be operated by those prepared to do serious work.

THE TELESCOPE

There is need to understand clearly certain fundamentals that do not seriously concern the visual observer of variable stars. Naturally the first is the telescope. A reflector is best. Useful photoelectric work can be done with a six-inch reflector on stars down to seventh magnitude. Of the sizes in common use by amateurs, twelve inches is a most useful aperture. This enables a wide range of stars to be observed commensurate with the expense and trouble in building the photometer.

The main requirements for the instrument are a rigid equatorial mounting and a reliable clock drive. It is an advantage to be able to use the instrument at the Cassegrain focus, since then there is the minimum of movement of the attached apparatus. However, whilst this is desirable it is not essential. Circles are an advantage but are not indispensable.

The telescope must be one that will form a good, sharp, star image. For the small instruments we are considering, the image must remain sharp with a diaphragm of the order of one millimeter. The test of the drive is that the image remains for ten minutes within 0.2 mm of the center of the diaphragm. A satisfactory finder suitable as a guide telescope is necessary.

SETTING THE TELESCOPE

It is assumed that the instrument has its optical parts correctly placed and adjusted, and that the tube is at right angles to the declination axis.

Before the equatorial head is adjusted make certain that the base on which the instrument is supported is horizontal. This can be done by means of a level placed at first in the meridian and then at right angles to the meridian.

The equatorial head is aligned on a meridian mark. This is done with a prismatic compass, allowing for the current magnetic variation of the observing site. The polar axis is then set to the correct elevation, which is, of course, the latitude of the observing site.

Detailed instructions abound in literature written for the amateur, concerning the accurate adjustment of an equatorial. There is no need to repeat these here. Those not familiar with such adjustments should consult Sidgwick 1954; Ingalls 1944, 1947.

COORDINATES

Declination (Dec.) and Right Ascension (R.A.) define a star's position in much the same way as any place on the Earth's surface is defined by its geographical latitude and longitude.

The declination of a star is its distance from the celestial equator, measured along the arc of the great circle, which passes through the star and the poles. It is measured in degrees and can be north (+) or south (−), according to the side of the celestial equator on which the star is situated.

The altitude of the celestial pole is equal to the latitude of the observer. So the declination of a star that passes directly overhead is equal to the geographical latitude of the observer. Thus Delta Canis Majoris (Dec. $-26° \, 19'$) passes directly overhead at Johannesburg (Latitude $-26° \, 11'$).

The celestial equator is half way between the north and south celestial poles and at right angles to the great circles from pole to pole. The point on the equator at which the Sun crosses it from south to north each year is called the March, or vernal, equinox. It is also known as the first point of Aries.

A star's right ascension is the arc of the equator from the vernal equinox to the foot of the perpendicular on the equator from the star. It is measured eastwards in hours, minutes and seconds of time, from 0 to 24 hours. As the rotation of the sky occupies 24 sidereal hours, conversion to angular units is easy. For instance, 1 hour = 15 degrees; 1 minute = $15'$ and 1 second = $15''$.

Figure 4–1 illustrates the points defined above.

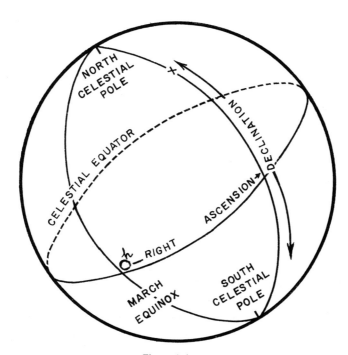

Figure 4–1.

PRECESSION

The right ascension and declination of a star change progressively. This is due to a long-term wobbling of the Earth's axis of rotation. This causes a slow displacement in the positions of the stars. The effect is known as precession.

As a result no position of a star is complete without the date of the epoch when the position applied. Thus catalogues and star atlases state, for instance, "Epoch 1900" or "Epoch 1950." This means that they are correct for the years 1900 and 1950 respectively, but such positions are accurate enough for use within ten years of these epochs.

Precession becomes important, when the position of a star is taken from a catalogue for one epoch, and it is desired to plot its position correctly on a chart for another epoch. A correction must be applied so that the position from the catalogue is brought to the epoch of the charts. Some catalogues provide details of such corrections. If they do not tables appear in most observing handbooks (see Norton 1943).

CHARTS

The two succeeding chapters provide suggestions on observing programs. From these the stars to be observed can be selected. Some of these variables will not be shown on the general charts available. It remains then to plot their positions on such charts, so that the observer has a finder chart that guides him to the region required. It is often necessary to make more detailed charts of the immediate vicinity of the variable, so that the variable and comparison star can be located with certainty. This is particularly important if the telescope has no circles.

The star maps readily available to amateurs and generally used by them are: Norton 1943; Becvar 1956; Becvar 1958, and Webb 1945. The epoch of the first three is 1950 and of the last 1920. Norton 1943 covers the entire sky to magnitude 6.35. Becvar 1956 also shows the entire sky and is complete to visual magnitude 7.75. Becvar 1958 covers only the region between Dec. $+30°$ and $-30°$. It is more complete than the other maps, since it shows the spectral types of all stars contained in the Yale Zone Catalogues. Variable stars, down to visual magnitude 10.0 at maximum brightness are shown. Webb 1945 shows stars down to ninth magnitude from the north celestial pole to Dec. $-23°$.

More detailed maps are Beyer & Graff 1950. This publication comprises 27 charts showing stars to 9.5 from the north pole to Dec. $-23°$. It is for the Epoch 1855, but the precession for 100 years is given. The *Bonner Durchmusterung* 1951 and 1954 are reproductions of the original maps by Schonfeld (Dec. $-2°$ to $-23°$) and Argelander (North Pole to $-2°$) for epoch 1855. The maps are complete to about magnitude 9.5. The Cordoba 1929 charts give the same coverage as the B.D. charts and extend from Dec. $-22°$ to the south pole. The epoch of the Cordoba charts is 1875.

Any observer should possess either Norton 1943 or Becvar 1956, as well as Becvar 1958. He will probably not be able to secure the B.D. or Cordoba charts, and the best he can hope for is to be allowed to copy the areas in which he is interested.

Across all the star maps mentioned above are a grid of lines marking R.A. and Declination. The epoch of the charts are stated on them. Before locating, or plotting, a variable on the charts, it is generally necessary to correct its catalogue position for precession.

Suppose it is desired to observe the eclipsing variable, ST Carinae. From Kukarkin's 1958 *Catalogue* its position is obtained for 1900 together with details of its annual precession. These are:

$$\text{R.A. (1900)} \quad 10\text{h } 12\text{m } 30\text{s} \quad \text{Prec. } +2^s04$$
$$\text{Dec. (1900)} \quad -59° \ 42.'9 \quad \quad -0.'298$$

We wish to plot the position of ST Carinae on Becvar 1956, for which the epoch is 1950. To the 1900 position of the variable we must apply corrections for 50 years precession. Thus:

$$\text{R.A. (1900)} \quad 10\text{h } 12\text{m } 30\text{s} + (2^s04 \times 50)$$
$$= 1\text{m } 42\text{s} = \text{R.A. (1950) } 10\text{h } 14\text{m } 12\text{s}$$
$$\text{Dec. (1900)} \quad -59° \ 42.'9 \quad -(0.298 \times 50)$$
$$= -14.'9 = \text{Dec. (1950) } -59° \ 57.'8$$

Suppose, instead of plotting the 1950 position, we had used the catalogue position for 1900. This would have lead us to identify wrongly ST Carinae, since there is another star at R.A. 10h 12m Dec. $-59°$ 43' in 1950.

If the position of the variable is required for the Cordoba charts we must bring the 1900 position back to 1875. As we are then working backwards the signs given above are reversed. Thus the 1875 position is:

R.A. (1900) 10h 12m 30s $-(2\overset{s}{.}04 \times 25) = -51s$
$$= (1875)\quad 10h\ 11m\ 39s$$
Dec. (1900) $-59°\ 42.'9\quad +(0.'298 \times 25) = +\ 7.'5$
$$= (1875)\quad -59°35.'4$$

It is quite possible that the observer may only have star maps that show stars to magnitude 7.75 and he is unable to identify a variable as faint as ST Carinae (Range 9.1 to 10.2 ptg) with certainty. His telescope has no circles. In this case he must know how to make his own chart.

The first thing to decide is the scale on which the chart is to be drawn. The scales in use for charts for visual observers are suitable. These are

Table 4-1
Scales in Right Ascension for Variable Star Charts.

Zone Dec.	'b' Chart	'd' Chart	Zone Dec.	'b' Chart	'd' Chart
0°	15	45	64°	6.6	19.7
5	15	44.8	65	6.3	19.0
10	14.8	44.3	66	6.1	18.3
15	14.5	43.6	68	5.6	16.9
20	14.1	42.3	70	5.1	15.4
25	13.6	40.8	72	4.6	13.9
30	13	39	74	4.1	12.4
35	12.3	36.9	75	3.9	11.7
40	11.5	34.5	76	3.6	10.9
42	11.2	33.5	77	3.4	10.1
44	10.8	32.4	78	3.1	9.4
45	10.6	31.8	79	2.9	8.6
46	10.4	31.3	80	2.6	7.8
48	10.0	30.1	81	2.3	7.0
50	9.6	28.9	82	2.2	6.7
52	9.2	27.7	83	1.8	5.5
54	8.8	26.5	84	1.6	4.7
55	8.6	25.8	85	1.3	3.9
56	8.4	25.2	86	1.0	3.1
58	8.0	23.9	87	0.8	2.4
60	7.5	22.5	88	0.5	1.6
62	7.0	21.1	89	0.2	0.79
			90	0.0	0.0

the "b" charts (60 seconds of arc equals 1 mm) and "d" (20 seconds of arc equals 1 mm). Naturally the separation of the lines marking successive minutes of R.A. changes with the declination. They are widest apart at the equator and gradually become narrower the further the star is away from the equator. Table 4–1 shows the scales for various declinations for both types of charts. Up to Dec. $\pm 40°$ it is only necessary to change the scale every 5°. From Dec. 40° to the Poles it is wiser to change more frequently. This table is one used by the V.S.S., R.A.S.N.Z. and was prepared by A. F. Jones.

The next step is to list from some convenient catalogue the stars that fall within the limits of the chart. For this purpose the *Henry Draper Catalogue* is the most convenient.

To make the method clear assume we desire to produce a chart on the "d" scale for ST Carinae. From the table we see that we must place the successive minutes of R.A. 22.5 mm apart. Obviously on the scale 15′ of declination is equal to 45 mm. A convenient chart will therefore show the stars for four minutes of R.A. on either side of the variable, and for 30′ of declination north and south of the variable.

From the *Henry Draper Catalogue* we find the following stars listed within these limits:

H. D.	R. A. (1900)	Dec. (1900)		Ptm. Mag.	Spec.	
88621	10h 8.0m	$-59°$	15′	9.0	A2	
22	8.0	59	28	9.0	K2	
23	8.0	60	06	9.5	A0	
48	8.2	59	23	9.1	B8	
62	8.3	60	15	9.48	K0	
88717	8.8	$-59°$	38′	9.5	B8	
33	8.9	59	27	8.9	B9	
88825	9.6	59	25	6.40	B3	
88934	10.3	59	46	7.9	A0	
89008	10.9	59	38	9.1	A3	
96	11.5	60	14	9.44	B	
89187	12.1	60	14	8.94	F5	
89202	12.3	59	48	9.5	A0	
18	12.4	60	12	9.54	A2	
34	12.5	59	43	Var.	A0	= ST Carinae
63	12.7	59	24	6.44	A2	
89614	15.3	59	54	9.1	A0	
25	15.4	59	15	9.0	B	
89701	15.9	60	03	9.94	A0	

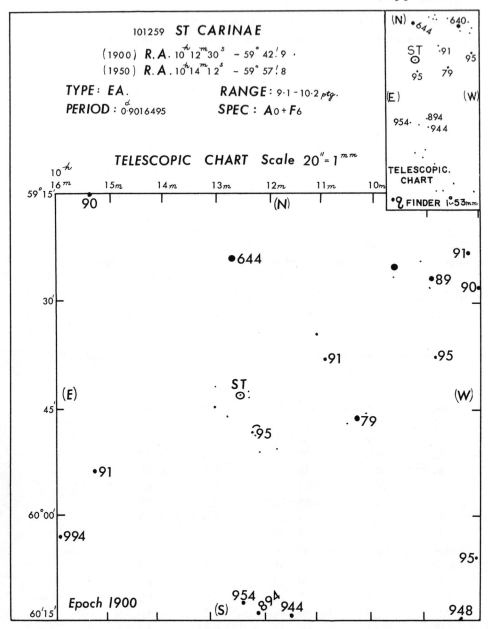

Figure 4–2. Chart for ST Carinae. A finder chart appears in the right-hand corner showing the relation of the field around ST Carinae to the bright naked-eye star q Carinae, seen in the south-east corner of the finder chart. In the main chart, stars from H. D. as listed in the text are shown by their H. D. photometric magnitudes with the decimal point omitted.

Figure 4–2 reproduces a chart for ST Carinae showing these stars. In the top righthand corner you will notice a finder chart showing the relation of ST Carinae and the field around it to the naked eye star, q Carinae. Obviously in a rich field especially, there are many more stars than appear in the Henry Draper Catalogue. These are normally taken from one of the *Durchmusterung* catalogues. In the example given the stars listed are sufficient to provide definite identification and this has been checked at the telescope.

A chart, such as this example, is all the observer without circles on his instrument requires. Provided his instrument has a reliable clock drive he can make the necessary observations.

It is essential that he knows how to hold his chart so that its orientation corresponds to the view in the telescope through the normal inverting eyepiece. The example has been prepared for use in the southern hemisphere, where it is usual to show North at the top of the chart. The west, or preceding edge, is then on the right; east, or following, on the left and south at the bottom. The chart is held so that the north point is directed towards the south celestial pole. In the northern hemisphere the reverse is true, i.e., the south point is directed towards the north celestial pole. Telescopic charts in the northern hemisphere usually have south at the top, east on the right, west on the left, and north at the bottom.

A universal rule, applying to both hemispheres, is first to let the stars drift through the field by their diurnal motion. This fixes the east-west line, since the stars come in on the east and pass out of the field on the west. Having determined the east-west line in the telescope, hold the chart so that its east-west line is parallel to, and in the same direction as, the east-west line in the field of view. This automatically aligns north and south correctly.

FINDING THE VARIABLE

It has been shown above how an observer without circles can produce a chart, which will enable him to identify the variable. He has also been shown how to orient his chart correctly. He may still have trouble in locating the variable.

Since you may have no knowledge of the brightness of the variable when you commence observing, the first essential to remember is that you are endeavoring to locate the field, *not the variable*. Study your chart before going to the telescope and note how the brighter stars tend to fall into groups. It is an advantage to connect these groups by lines so that you can readily see that they form triangles, rectangles and other patterns. In forming such patterns do not include the variable itself. Work from a bright star as shown on your finder chart, sweeping toward the field and identifying the stars on the finder chart. Then watch for the patterns you have marked on your chart. After identifying these you can easily locate the variable. Detailed instructions are given by Bateson 1958.

An instrument with reliable circles enables the variable to be found first and checked with a chart afterwards. A skilled amateur, however, rarely uses circles since he is able, through his intimate knowledge of the sky and his charts, to locate variables much quicker than by using circles.

Probably many readers will lack this skill and will prefer to use circles. There are two methods used. The first does not require any knowledge of sidereal time. Select a bright naked eye star, reasonably close to the variable. Obtain its position from a star catalogue.

Suppose for locating ST Carinae we use q Carinae. The 1900 positions of the two objects are:

q Carinae	R.A. 10h 13.7m	Dec.	$-60°$	50'
ST Carinae	10 12.5		-59	43
Difference	1.2m		$1°$	07'

Thus ST Carinae lies 1° 7' north of q Carinae and 1.2 minutes west.

Now center q Carinae in the field of view. Clamp the R.A. axis. Then move the telescope 1° 7' north in declination, reading from the declination circle. Now clamp the declination axis and unclamp the R.A. axis. Move the telescope 1.2 m west as read on the hour circle.

The accuracy of this method depends on the accuracy of the circles. Generally it is good enough with a low power to bring the variable into the field. If the circles are finely graduated and of a good standard the method is sufficiently accurate for use with moderate powers. But never assume that you have the right star. Always check the field with your chart.

The second method requires sidereal time. Usually the amateur observer has no sidereal clock. The simplest way to obtain the sidereal time is to take some convenient time early in the evening, say 7:00 P.M. standard time. Find the local sidereal time (L.S.T.) corresponding to this. For this purpose take the current year's Astronomical Ephemeris. You will find there the sidereal time for the Greenwich meridian for every day of the year at 0 hours U.T. To this are added three figures.

As an example, assume we require the local sidereal time in longitude 159° 47′ west (+ 10h 39m) at 7:00 P.M. (i.e., 19 hours) local mean solar time on 1960 July 7.

(a) Greenwich mean sideral time, 0 h U.T. Juli 7	18h	59m	50.725 s
(b) Reduction for longitude		1	44.971
(c) Local mean solar time	19	00	00
(d) Reduction of local mean time to sidereal interval		3	07.273
	38	4	42.969
Discarding excess 24 hours	24		
Local Mean Sidereal Time (L.S.T.)	14h	4m	42.969 s.

The Astronomical Ephemeris provides a Table (No. 1X) from which (b) and (d) above are taken. All you have to do is to add.

Since you have no sidereal clock set an ordinary clock or watch to the result at 7:00 P.M. local time. The ordinary clock will be sufficiently accurate to serve for the evening's observing. As these read only to twelve hours you must remember to add twelve hours to the face time, when the sideral time is greater than twelve hours.

If you wish you can obtain your L.S.T. direct from the stars. Select some well-known star on or near the equator and ascertain its position from the Ephemeris. Point the telescope due south in the northern hemisphere, or due north in the southern hemisphere. Clamp it in declination equal to the declination of the star. Provided the star selected is just east of the meridian, it will soon come into view. When the star is in the centre of the field set your clock to the R.A. of the star. This is your sidereal time at that instant.

Having found your L.S.T., you are now ready to set your circles. To do this you first find the hour angle of the star from the equation:

Hour angle (H.A.) = Sidereal Time − Right Ascension

If the sidereal time is greater than the right ascension, the star has passed the meridian and the hour angle is west, or positive. If the sidereal time is less than the right ascension, the star has not yet crossed the meridian and the hour angle is east, or negative. To perform the subtraction you may have to add 24 hours to the sidereal time, but the resulting hour angle must always be less than twelve hours.

When the telescope is set in the meridian, and the circles are in adjustment, the R.A. circle will read 0 hours. To find the star clamp the telescope in the declination of the star. Then, unclamping the R.A. axis, turn the instrument east or west until the Hour Angle as read on the R.A. circle is the H.A. of the star.

Should your instrument have a movable hour circle marked from 0 to 24 hours, select any bright star. Turn the circle to read its R.A. Then turn the telescope until the hour circle reads the R.A. of the star you are seeking.

SELECTING A COMPARISON STAR

Having located the variable, you select a suitable comparison star from the list already prepared. This should be close to the variable, which is not however always possible. It should be of the same approximate magnitude and spectral class. Sometimes it is necessary to try two or more stars from the list before obtaining a suitable one.

Assume, once again, that we are observing ST Carinae. From the list of nearby stars, given earlier in this chapter, we might select H.D. 89218. Its photometric magnitude is given as 9.54 and since its spectral type is A2 it should be constant. It might prove to be too bright and, in that case, we might select H.D. 89701, magnitude 9.94, spectral type A0.

SELECTING A CHECK STAR

Normally we avoid stars of the late spectral types, since they are often variable. Even stars of type K are often slightly variable. So that we can be certain that our comparison star is no–variable we also select a check star. This should be one that complies with the same conditions as laid down for the comparison star.

OBSERVING

The technique used in making the actual observations varies fairly widely among different observers. One method is suggested here. Observers may prefer another method, but it should be remembered that having determined the routine to be followed, it must be strictly adhered to on all occasions.

Set up the equipment about an hour before observing commences and turn on the amplifier. This permits the dark current of the photo-multiplier to settle down. It will drift, fast at first, but gradually settles to a stable level, although it is never stationary. Having identified the variable, comparison star, and check star, take a few trial deflections on both the variable and the comparison star to see that they come within the range of the meter. If the comparison star does not prove suitable you may have to select another star from your list that gives readings within the range of the meter. It is more convenient to have an assistant to make the recordings while you operate the telescope.

First set the pointer, by means of the zero adjustment, at some suitable point. This should be low on the scale. Now commence by measuring the sky brightness. To do this set the telescope on a nearby region of the sky as clear of stars as possible. Take a dark reading in order to check the dark current. Then open the slide and record the sky. Fifteen seconds later read the meter, close the dark slide and record your meter reading. Make three of these sky readings, keeping to the 15-second intervals. A series of this nature is termed a set. End the set with a dark reading.

Follow the first set on the sky, by a set of four deflections of the comparison star. This will involve nine meter readings, since you start and finish with a dark reading and the readings on the comparison star are separated by a dark reading. You have then recorded four deflections of the comparison star and five dark readings. You do the same with the variable. You must also record the standard time, to the nearest half minute, of the middle reading of each set. As soon as the set with the variable is completed move back to the comparison star and take another set of that star. Thus you straddle the observations of the variable with those of the comparison star.

Measure the sky about every half hour under normal conditions. It may be necessary, for instance during the rising or setting of the Moon, to make sky readings every ten minutes. You continue the observations as long as you can if the variable is a very rapid one. In that event you may even obtain a complete light curve during one night's work. On a slow variable generally observations need not last more than an hour.

You now have a mass of readings that at first appear to you as a hopeless tangle. However, when they are reduced they will start to make sense. The first step is to find the mean of the first two dark readings of a set. Substract this from the first slide open reading. Then find the mean of the next two dark readings and substract this mean from the second slide open reading. In forming the means of the dark readings remember that each time one dark reading is used over again. You now have the four readings of each set with the mean dark readings deducted from them. Now find the mean of all the deflections in each set.

Take the means that you have found for the sky sets and plot these against the time of observation. Through the points plotted draw a smooth curve and from this read the value of the sky deflection at the time of each set on the comparison star and variable. This value is subtracted from each set. From the mass of figures you originally had you are now left with a series of mean deflections of comparison star, variable, comparison star continued in that order until the end of the observations.

REDUCTION

The mean deflections with which you are left are proportional to the brightnesses of the two stars being compared. It is always possible that between the observations of the comparison star preceding those of the variable and the observations of the comparison star following those of the variable, there was a change in atmospheric transparency. All you can do is average the two consecutive sets of the comparison star. You assume that the mean so derived represents the apparent brightness of the comparison star at the time the variable was measured. In forming these means, each set on the comparison star is used twice, except the first and last.

You now have a series of groups of three numbers. These give the standard time or U.T. (whichever you used), mean deflection on the comparison star and mean deflection on the variable. The rations of the two mean deflections should be converted into magnitude differences and these can then be plotted against time to show how the variable changed.

JULIAN DATE

Before proceding it is an advantage to transfer the series of standard times (or U.T.) into Julian days and decimals of a day. Julian dates are used since they form a continuous series of dates unbroken into years and months. Hence they form a most convenient means of calculating periods with the minimum amount of trouble.

It is first necessary to convert your local time (or U.T. if you recorded in U.T.) to Greenwich Mean Astronomical Time (G.M.A.T.) which is reckoned from midday. G.M.A.T. is twelve hours behind U.T. As an example N.Z. Mean Time is twelve hours fast on U.T., which is twelve hours ahead of G.M.A.T. So to convert N.Z.M.T. to G.M.A.T. deduct one day. Then read off the Julian Date from the Julian calendar to be found in most handbooks and which is also distributed by most Variable Star organisations. An abbreviated table, giving the JD for the first of each year, is found in the Appendix. Tables for converting the hours, minutes and seconds to decimals of a day appear in the current Astronomical Ephemerides.

Thus an observation made on 1960 July 2 at 22h 12m 30s G.M.A.T. is J.D. 2,437,118.925347.

EXTINCTION CORRECTIONS

This correction is due to the attenuation of light passing through the atmosphere. It is at a minimum at the zenith. Normally it increases very rapidly from a Zenith Distance of 45° to the horizon. For this reason observations at low altitudes are undesirable.

It must be admitted that the normal extinction correction is at its best a well-informed guess. One method is to select a star that passes close to the zenith. The relative magnitudes of such a star are measured for different zenith distances during the night. These magnitudes are plotted against zenith distance. It is assumed that at the zenith the extinction is zero. Since we are only concerned with differences in extinction this assumption is valid. It is also assumed that the extinction is the same at the same zenith distance in all directions. This is often not so, due to variation in seeing, high clouds, and other causes. In measuring the relative magnitudes of any one star to determine the extinction correction for the night we also assume that the atmosphere has remained much the same in all directions. Such an assumption is erroneous.

Since our observations consist usually in comparing the variable with a nearby constant star the extinction correction can be neglected. This assumes that the difference in zenith distance between the two stars is so small as to make their differential atmospheric extinction neglible. If the stars are far apart, however, a correction must be applied and this can be done by means of the formula given later in this chapter.

REDUCTION TO THE SUN

A further correction is necessary to adjust the times of observation to the sun. This makes your observations strictly comparable with observations made elsewhere of the same star. This is called the heliocentric correction. Whilst unimportant for long period variables it becomes important for short period stars, which change in brightness within a few hours. The time taken by light to travel from the earth to the mean sun is 8.31 minutes. That is the amount of the correction necessary if the variable is on the ecliptic and at opposition.

This is generally not the case, so a reduction formula must be used. This is given later. If the amateur desires to avoid such corrections he can fit his instrument with a decimal of a day clock, as described by W.Blitztein, J.K.Thorpe and F.B.Wood in *Sky and telescope*, July 1951. By precomputing the heliocentric correction for the star the clock can be set to read heliocentric time at the start of a night's run. This enables the heliocentric time in decimals of a day to be read directly from an indicator.

SUMMARY

As a result of following the instructions the observer now has a series of numbers representing his observations. The first number of each set gives the Julian date and decimals of a day representing the date and time of each observation. The second gives the mean deflection on the comparison star and the third the mean deflection of the variable. Such a series is uncorrected for atmospheric extinction (if the observations warrant such a correction). They also have to be converted to heliocentric time. In addition it is necessary to convert the mean deflections into magnitude differences and to plot these differences against time or phase to produce a light curve.

Faced with an array of reductions the average amateur decides that the work is too long and involved. As a result, while he is interested in making the observations, he feels that their use is beyond his time and capabilities. So he gives up all thought of doing photoelectric work.

There is no need for this. Anyone with reliable photoelectric observations will find no trouble in getting assistance with the reductions. Observatories engaged in such work are generally pleased to assist. The headquarters of the various amateur variable star organisations (BAA, VSS,R.A.S.N.Z., A.A.V.S.O. etc) are pleased to take over such observations and reduce them. For the few amateurs keen enough to do their own reductions we now give some directions.

REDUCTION

Differential Atmospheric Extinction

Determine first the zenith distances of the variable and the comparison star. This is best done by solution of the spherical triangle using the formula:

$$\cos z = \sin \varphi \sin \delta + \cos \varphi \cos \delta \cos H$$

where

z denotes the zenith distance.
φ the observer's latitude
δ the star's declination
H the star's hour angle

We already know these quantities except the zenith distance.
The formula for atmospheric extinction is

$$\Delta m = 0.35 \; (\sec z_1 - \sec z_2)$$
$$= 0.35 \sec z_1 - 0.35 z_2$$

This represents the difference in magnitude to be added to the star nearest the zenith. z_1 and z_2 are the zenith distances of the two stars. An observational constant, 0.35, is an average value and sufficient for all but the most precise work.

It is now necessary to compute a table of $\sin \varphi \sin \delta + \cos \varphi \cos \delta \cos H$ for each star, using H as the argument and plot two curves with 0.35 sec z as ordinates and H in degrees as abscissae. Knowing the hour angle of each star pick out from the curves the corresponding ordinates. The difference is the difference in magnitude required.

Conversion to Heliocentric Time

The formula is

$$\text{Hel.–Geo.} = 8\text{m } 31\text{s } [R \cos \beta \cos (\Theta - \lambda)]$$
$$= [-8.31R \cos \Theta \, (\cos \beta \cos \lambda)] + [-8.31R \sin \Theta \, (\cos \beta \sin \lambda)]$$

where

R = actual distance of the earth from the sun in astronomical units
β = latitude of the star referred to the ecliptic system
Θ = position of the earth on ecliptic referred to the vernal equinox
λ = longitude of star on ecliptic.

Tables are available showing the values of 8.31 R cos Θ and 8.31 R sin Θ. To compute cos β cos λ and cos β sin λ use

$$\cos \beta \cos \lambda = \cos \delta \cos \alpha$$
$$\cos \beta \sin \lambda = \sin \varepsilon \sin \delta + \cos \varepsilon \cos \delta \sin \alpha$$

where

ε = inclination of the ecliptic = $23° \, 27'$
δ = declination of star
α = R.A. of star.

Reducing Ratio of Brightness to Magnitude Differences

Suppose we have compared Algol with Alpha Persei and have the following result:

$$A = \text{Alpha Persei, deflection } 7.46$$
$$B = \text{Algol, deflection } 6.33$$

then

$$\frac{A}{B} = \rho^{\Delta m}$$

$$\Delta m = \frac{\log 7.46 - \log 6.33}{0.4}$$

$$= \frac{0.072}{0.4}$$

$$= 0.18 \text{ mag}$$

This formula is based on Pogson's rule that a star of one magnitude is 2.512 times as bright as a star of the next lower magnitude. This relation is generally known as ρ. Pogson decided arbitrarily to adopt the value 0.4 for log ρ on account of its convenience as a divisor and thus made ρ equal to 2.512.

LIGHT ELEMENTS

Sometimes we are fortunate with a very short period variable in being able to obtain sufficient observations in one night's work to provide a complete light curve of the star. Normally however this is not possible with stars having periods greater than a few hours. It then becomes necessary to combine observations over several cycles to form one standard light curve.

Since Campbell and Jacchia 1941 have set out the methods very clearly for amateur investigators there is no need to repeat the instructions here. The only remark called for is to state that the magnitude differences that we have recorded are treated in the same way as actual magnitudes.

Finally the observer who reduces his observations to this stage will find it worth while to consult some of the professional papers detailing observations and their reduction. The *Astronomical Journal*, March 1959, contains observations, light curves, and a discussion by Binnendijk of two W Ursae Majoris variables. These are a model of how observations can be dealt with and show readily the value of photoelectric observation. There is no reason why amateurs cannot follow in the footsteps of the professionals and produce results that are equally as accurate and useful.

REFERENCES

Bateson, F. M. 1958. *The Observations of Variable Stars*, published by the author, Rarotonga.

Becvar, A. 1956. *Atlas Coeli 1950.0*, Praha. Available from Sky Publishing Co., Cambridge, Mass.

———. 1958. *Atlas Eclipticalis 1950.0*, Praha. Available from Sky Publ. Co Cambridge, Mass.

Beyer, M., & Graff, K. 1950. *Stern-Atlas fur 1855.0*. Ferd Dummlers Verlag, Bonn.

Binnendijk, L. 1959. "Photoelectric Light Curves of V566 Ophiuchi & AB Andromedae." A. J. 64, No. 2, p. 65.

Bonner Durchmusterung. 1951. "Atlas der Himmelszone zwischen 1 ° und 23 ° sudlicher Declination." Ferd. Drummlers Verlag, Bonn.

———. 1954. "Atlas des Nordlichen gestirnten Himmels fur den Anfang des Jahres 1855." Ferd. Drummlers Verlag, Bonn.

Campbell, L., & Jacchia, L. 1941. *The Story of Variable Stars*. Blakiston Co., Philadelphia.

Cordoba. 1929. *Zonas de Exploracion del Cielo Austral Atlas*, Cordoba Observatory.

Ingalls, A. G. 1944. *Amateur Telescope Making Advanced*. Munn & Co., Inc.

———. 1947. *Amateur Telescope Making* (4th ed.). Munn & Co., Inc.

Kukarkin, Parenago, Efremov, & Kholopov 1958. *General Catalogue of Variable Stars* (2nd ed.). Moscow.

Norton, A. P. 1943. *A Star Atlas & Reference Handbook (Epoch 1950)* (9th ed.). Gall & Inglis, London.

Sidwick, J. B. 1954. *Amateur Astronomer's Handbook*." Faber & Faber Ltd., London.

Webb, H. B. 1945. *Webbs Atlas of the Stars (Epoch 1920)*. Published by the author.

CHAPTER 5

Intrinsic Variable Stars

BY HELMUT A. ABT

Kitt Peak National Observatory

The study of intrinsic variable stars has been one of the most active fields in astronomy for more than a hundred years. In fact there are very few observational astronomers who have not worked on such stars. From this one would think that we know a great deal about why and how stars pulsate and explode and why some do and others do not. But the fact is that progress has been slow and our understanding is rudimentary.

One reason for this lack of progress is that the pertinent observations could not be made until the advent of modern techniques such as photoelectric filter photometry, fast cameras, and simultaneous high-dispersion spectroscopy. Furthermore we had to wait for the development of theoretical astrophysics, particularly concerning the interiors and atmospheres of stars. The third reason is that the observations of intrinsic variables have often not been planned efficiently. Confronted with some ten thousand variables, too many astronomers have acted as though our general aim is simply to obtain a first-class light curve of each one, rather than to concentrate on a few or to obtain the kinds of observations that would yield the most information on their nature, origin, location, and behavior.

Intrinsic variables are stars that vary by themselves in brightness and most other characteristics such as radius and color. The next chapter will be concerned with stars that are usually constant in brightness by themselves but that have companions that intervene on the line of sight; these are called geometrical or eclipsing variable stars.

The most common kind of intrinsic variable star is the pulsating star, that is, one whose radius oscillates with time. This type of expansion and contraction is usually periodic, either very accurately so or roughly so. As such a star contracts, its atmosphere becomes compressed and hotter and hence gives off more light per square mile. The total brightness of a star depends on the amount of surface area and the amount of light given off by each unit of area. In pulsating stars both of these vary with time but the second usually wins out: the star is usually brightest when it is nearly at its smallest size.

Another kind of intrinsic variable is the exploding star, such as the novae. In an exploding star the surface layer is abruptly and permanently thrown off. The sudden increase in size of the surface causes a sudden increase in brightness of the star. As this layer expands it gradually becomes transparent and we again see the small star at its center, shining at the rate it did before the outburst.

A third kind of variable star may be the spotted stars, ones in which parts of the surface are brighter than other parts and rotation brings these alternately in view. It has been suggested that the magnetic variables are of this kind.

Intrinsic variables have been studied for two general reasons. One is as an aid to galactic and extragalactic structure studies. Some of these variables have very useful characteristics. For instance, it was found that all stars with certain distinctly shaped light curves and a certain range in period have the same intrinsic brightness; thus their distances—and hence the distances of the clusters or galaxies in which they may be imbedded—can be determined from their brightnesses. A second reason for studying intrinsic variables is to learn more about the mechanism and occurrence of pulsation and explosion.

There are roughly twenty kinds of intrinsic variables. Table 5-1 gives a brief résumé of some of the characteristics of the major classes. From the first column it is seen that the class name is often derived from the name of the brightest or first-known star of that kind. The subclass depends on the shape of the light curves (Eggen or Bailey types), the velocities in our galaxy (high or low), or unusual spectral features. The Baade population types refer to (I) young stars located mainly in spiral arms and young clusters and (II) old stars found throughout ours and other old galaxies.

Some variables tend to vary simultaneously with two or more periods, just as the height of the ocean waves at one place on the earth varies with the periods of revolution of the sun and moon around the earth. In the case of a star whose light curve is rather erratic there is always the question whether this is due to the superposition of quite a number of individual periods or whether it is truly a random (non-periodic) effect. Column four of Table 5-1 lists whether the stars are strictly periodic (regular), semiregular, or irregular and column six lists the secondary periods.

An informative way to classify stars is by their surface temperatures and luminosities. A star's temperature can usually be obtained from its color or the appearance of its spectrum. In stars of successively lower temperatures their spectra are classified as types O, B, A, F, G, K, and M. The intrinsic luminosity (absolute magnitude) of a star is known only if we know its distance; it is expressed as its apparent magnitude if it were moved to a distance of 10 parsecs from the sun. Columns seven and eight of Table 5-1 give the spectral types and luminosities of the various classes of variables and Figures 5-1 and 5-2 show their distribution in the color-luminosity diagrams for the two population types.

The large number of question marks in Table 5-1 already illustrates the gaps in our knowledge and the need for well-directed work. The last column of the table contains references to review articles or, in the absence of these, to articles which will start a researcher on the path to tracing down the literature on those variables.

The remaining part of this chapter gives specific projects which need to be done and can be done with the equipment and background which many amateurs have or can obtain. These topics are of current interest; ten or twenty years from now we shall have answers to most of these problems and yet other problems will become urgent. Astronomy does not stand still while one person hesitates to act!

The techniques to be employed are similar to those described in Chapters 4 and 6: either a variable is compared with a nearby "comparison" star of nearly the same color and apparent magnitude or absolute photometry is carried out. The former is easier and sufficient in most of the following projects. However it is often desireable to standardize the filters used by observing some standard stars.

A few words about honesty should be written. Some stars show rapid bursts, depressions, or irregularities which may be important. If a person were to eliminate arbitrarily or change observations simply because "they don't seem to fit," he would not only publish false information but he might be missing important results. Whenever it is found that a person has changed some observations to make them look better, all his previous observations are immediately held suspect and valueless. In the field of intrinsic variable stars observations often increase in value with age. Don't lose out on a lasting reputation for the sake of some temporary recognition.

Table 5-1
Classes of Intrinsic Variable Stars

Class	Subclass	Pop.	Regularity	Fundemental period (days)	Secondary period (days)
1. Short Period Variables	——	I	semi.	.08–.19	.07–.24
2. β Canis Majoris	——	I	semi.	.15–.25	.16–.26
3. Cepheids	Eggen A,B,C,	I	reg.	1–50	none
4. Long Period Variables	high, low velocity	I, II	semi.	90–700	?
5. Semi-Regular	——	I, II	semi.	4–2000	yes
6. Hubble-Sandage	——	I	irreg.	years	?
7. Peculiar A	Si, Sr, Mn, Cr-Eu	I	semi. or irreg.	1–226	?
8. T Tauri	various	I	irreg.	?	?
9. RR Lyrae	Bailey a,b,c,	II	semi.	.08–1.0	yes
10. W Virginis	——	II	semi.	1–40	?
11. RV Tauri	high, low velocity	II	semi.	40–150	yes
12. Dwarf novae	U Gem Z Cam SS Cyg	II	semi.	∼50	?
13. R Coronae Borealis	——	?	semi.	10–100	?
14. Novae	——	II	semi.	$10–10^6(?)$ yr.	?
15. Supernovae	I, II	I, II	?	?	?
16. Flare stars	——	?	?	?	?
17. Symbolic stars	——	?	irreg.	?	?
18. B emission	——	I	irreg.	?	?

Table 5–I (continued)

Spectral type	Luminosity	Reference
1. A4–F5	$+3$ to 0	Eggen (1957)
2. B0.5–B2	-3 to -5	Struve (1955)
3. F5–K0	-3 to -6	Eggen (1951)
4. M0–M8, C, S	-3 to -1	Payne-Gaposchkin (1951)
5. B–M	$+1$ to -9	Abt (1957)
6. Fe	-8 to -9	Hubble and Sandage (1953)
7. B8–F0	-1 to $+2$	Babcock (1958)
8. A–M	above Main Sequence	Herbig (1952) Herbig (1957)
9. A0–F2	0 to $+1$	Preston (1959)
10. F2–G5	-1 to -3	Joy (1949)
11. F2–K4	-3 to -4	Joy (1952)
12. G–K	$+5$ to $+9$	Joy (1954)
13. F–K	——	Payne-Gaposchkin (1957)
14. early	$+4$	Aller (1954a) Payne-Gaposchkin (1957)
15. ?	at max.: -13 to -17	Payne-Gaposchkin (1957)
16. K6e–M6e	$+11$ to $+16$	Struve (1959)
17. M+early	?	Aller (1954b)
18. Be	-2 to -5	Aller (1954a) Merrill and Burwell (1949)

FLARE STARS

Among the cool dwarf stars are some that have short-lived outbursts in brightness. Typically such a star may increase in brightness by a magnitude for five minutes. These outbursts may be similar to solar flares and it has been suggested that the accompanying radio emission may be detectable. Perhaps even the diffuse background of radio noise in our galaxy may be from the sporatic outbursts of millions of flare stars. Projects with large radio telescopes are being planned to detect radio-frequency flares in flare stars but their success will depend on knowing more about the optical activity of these stars.

How often does a flare star have an outburst? What is the distribution of brightnesses of the outbursts? Does an unusually bright outburst follow an unusually long quiescent period as though the star were saving up energy for a big splash? This last question needs long continuous observing runs, perhaps even cooperative programs between observers at several widely different longitudes so that a star can be followed on a 24-hour basis. Such cooperative programs could be coordinated with the use of amateur radio sets. Does the color of the star change during an outburst? This needs rapid-fire work, preferrably with a photometer which can measure magnitudes through two filters simultaneously by means of beam splitters and two photomultipliers. How long do outbursts last, on the average, and what are the accurate shapes of ourbursts? Do the lower-luminosity flare stars have more or less intense outbursts? These questions can be answered with observations in one color, perhaps, but they require many observations of outbursts so that the averages are meaningful. A convenient list of known flare stars is given by Struve (1959). Do all dwarf M emission (dMe) stars show flares? A list of dMe stars is given by Joy (1947).

PECULIAR A-TYPE MAGNETIC VARIABLES

Among the stars of spectral type A are some which have very peculiar spectra. These look as though some of the most abundant elements in their atmospheres are such normally rare elements as europium or strontium. It was found by Dr. Horace Babcock that these stars invariably have strong magnetic fields in their atmospheres.

Probably the magnetic fields induce nuclear reactions which produce, as in cyclotrons, the strange elements. In most of these stars the strength of the magnetic field (as well as the light, color, appearance of the spectrum, radial velocity, and all other measureable quantities) varies in either a periodic or random fashion. This may be due to rotation or pulsation or both. But to measure a magnetic field at one time requires the use of one of the largest telescopes in the world and many hours of measurement and reduction of the observations, while photometry of the same stars can be done with moderate-sized telescopes and can be just as useful in hunting for a period. Babcock (1960) has published a plea for such kinds of photometry and gave references to lists of stars.

In addition to the results for each star that can be obtained through photometry, there are many questions that need answers. These can be obtained mostly from the light and color curves. What fraction of the magnetic variables are periodic? What is the average period and range in period for these stars? What are the average light and color ranges? Are most periodic magnetic variables accurately regular in their behavior? Is the range in light (or color) correlated with the range in magnetic field? The light ranges are typically only a tenth of a magnitude and the periods are usually several days in length, so consistently accurate photometry is necessary. Are there any eclipsing binaries among the peculiar A magnetic stars?

Another type of observation that needs to be done is to measure photometrically the changes in the spectral features. Deutsch (1947) shows illustrations of some typical changes in line intensities. These changes (in the stronger lines) could be measured with a photoelectric photometer and interference filters that transmit only a narrow wavelength region centered on a spectral line and, for control, on a nearby clear region. A photometer with a beam splitter and two photomultipliers that allows simultaneous measures on and off the line is much more accurate and can be used even through several magnitudes of clouds and haze. This is an excellent type of photometer for observers in regions of poor sky conditions. It could be used on many other projects with other sets of filters. Such a photometer is described by Crawford (1958). Interference filters, however, are rather expensive (about $50 each); they are custom-made for particular wavelengths by Baird Atomic Co., Cambridge, Mass., and other companies.

SECONDARY PERIODS IN PULSATING STARS

In some classes of pulsating stars (e.g., RR Lyrae, β Canis Majoris, Short Period Variables) most members have secondary periods. We do not know why some stars try to pulsate in two periods and others in just one. McNamara and Hansen (1961) have suggested that among the β Canis Majoris stars the nonrotating stars have just one period while rotation induces a secondary period. We do not know whether there is a relation between the size of the secondary period and of the fundamental one in all classes, although in the Short Period Variables Fitch (1959) found a relation. A great deal more information is needed and the first step is to determine the secondary periods.

If a star has just one period its light curve is the same in cycle after cycle. If it has a second one which is close to the fundamental period, the amplitude of the light curve will slowly vary with a beat period whose reciprocal is the difference of the reciprocals of the two periods. The phenonoma is familiar in musical notes that are extremely close in pitch. To determine a secondary period it is necessary to observe at least several dozen cycles. If the beat period is long and the fundamental period is a fraction of a day (as in all three classes mentioned above), observations made during several successive nights can be combined to form a light curve for one phase in the beat period.

The greatest need for data on secondary periods is among the RR Lyrae stars. About 2,425 such stars are known, so there are enough for everybody to work on! These stars and all known variables are listed in the most important books of variable star observers, the *General Catalogue of Variable Stars*, Volumes I and II, by B. V. Kukarkin, P. P. Parenago, Iu. I. Efremov, and P. N. Kholopov. These are available from Telberg Book Co., 544 Sixth Avenue, New York 11, New York. Don't let the fact that they are in Russian scare you; where necessary the English equivalents or translations have been courteously provided. The catalogue lists, among many other things, the star names, position, magnitudes, fundamental periods, and, if they are known, the secondary periods. In Table 5–2 we have abstracted from this catalogue the RR Lyrae stars brighter than 11.0 magnitude at all times.

Table 5-2
RR Lyrae Stars Brighter than 11.0 Magnitude

Star	α	δ	m_{ptg} *		Ephemeris	
		(1960)	max.	min.	Epoch	Period
	h m	° ′				d
RU Scl	0 0.7	−25 10.1	9.4	10.9	2427403.177 +	0.4933239 E
SW And	0 21.6	+29 10.8	8.8	10.4	18132.7913	.4422792156
RU Psc	1 12.2	+24 12.3	9.8	10.5	29290.8340	.39040
RR Cet	1 30.1	+ 1 8.3	9.2	10.3	17501.4421	.5530253
SS For	2 6.1	−27 3.2	9.0	10.0	27415.210	.49543107
X Ari	3 6.3	+10 17.9	9.0	9.9	20785.635	.6511248
SV Eri	3 10.0	−11 30.3	9.3	9.9	26590.319	.7137306
BC Eri	4 45.2	−14 41.5	9.7	10.8	28869.791	.26389458
RX Eri	4 47.9	−15 48.4	8.4	9.4	27386.412	.5872450
U Lep	4 54.6	−21 16.5	10.1	10.8	15013.353	.58147136
RY Col	5 13.9	−41 40.3	9.50v	10.85v	34310.565	.478859
BB Pup	8 22.6	−19 25.6	10.0v	10.9v	31169.167	.480124
RZ Pyx	8 50.4	−27 19.9	8.6v	9.3v	28542.162	.4888
TT Lyn	9 0.5	+44 44.8	9.3	10.	35599.30	.39225
DK Vel	9 16.0	−52 54.9	10.7	11.0	29778.283	.415690
T Sex	9 51.4	+ 2 14.9	9.9v	10.6v	27458.463	.3246717
WY Ant	10 14.2	−29 31.1	9.8	10.8		.57431216
TU UMa	11 27.7	+30 17.4	9.3	10.3	25760.441	.557665
SU Dra	11 35.7	+67 33.2	9.4	10.5	20605.7569	.66041926
UU Vir	12 6.5	− 0 15.8	9.8	10.7	19505.314	.47560558
SW Dra	12 16.0	+69 43.9	9.8	11.0	26224.5888	.56967021
YZ Boo	13 52.0	+17 26.6	10.30v	10.80v		.104
V499 Cen	13 52.8	−43 2.6	9.7	10.7	28336.32	.34666
W CVn	14 4.8	+38 1.0	10.0	10.9	21077.985	.551758
EH Lib	14 56.9	− 0 47.5	9.5	10.1	33438.6076	.0884139
AP Ser	15 12.1	+10 8.1	10.4	10.9	28334.279	.2539012
VY Ser	15 29.0	+ 1 49.0	9.5	10.7	31225.341	.71409384
UV Oct	16 22.5	−83 49.3	9.8v	10.7v	34328.396	.542625
VX Her	16 28.9	+18 26.7	9.8	11.0	21750.486	.45537152
DY Her	16 29.4	+12 5.4	10.27	10.94	33439.4865	.14863142
AT Her(?)	17 35.0	+44 59.0	10.3	10.8		.33:
V703 Sco	17 39.7	−32 30.5	7.7	7.9	28344.323	.1152803
XZ Dra	19 9.5	+64 47.4	9.2v	10.4v	27985.648	.4764944
RR Lyr	19 24.2	+42 42.3	6.94	8.03	14856.408	.56683735
V440 Sgr	19 29.9	−23 56.4	9.2	10.5	26581.203	.477474
XZ Cyg	19 31.7	+56 18.0	8.7	10.35	34951.456	.4665839
BP Vul	20 23.8	+20 54.0	9.5	10.6		.64063:
DX Del	20 45.6	+12 18.8	9.4	10.1	25807.494	.47261498
V Ind	21 8.9	−45 14.3	9.2	10.2	27993.567	.479591
RS Gru	21 40.5	−48 12.4	7.65v	8.22v	35399.059	.1470143
DE Lac	22 8.4	+40 43.3	10.7	11.0	28807.132	.2536937
DH Peg	22 13.4	+ 6 37.1	9.2	10.2	27695.342	.25551267
RZ Cep	22 37.8	+64 38.6	9.2	9.8	29162.552	.30867872
BH Peg	22 51.0	+15 34.0	10.3	11.0	26596.535	.64101381
DY Peg	23 6.9	+16 59.8	10.11	10.88	34696.3966	.072926358
DN Aqr	23 17.1	−24 26.3	10.	10.5	28433.4436	.38759
BS Aqr	23 46.7	− 8 22.1	8.8	9.2	2428095.261 +	0.197826 E

* Visual apparent magnitudes are designated with a "v."

PERIOD CHANGES IN PULSATING STARS

No star stays forever at one place in the color-magnitude diagram. Since stars are giving off energy (produced in nuclear transformations) at colossal rates, they must be undergoing changes in composition. The changes gradually cause the stars to change their radii and surface temperatures and hence their absolute magnitudes. For instance, a star at the upper end of the Main Sequence (see Fig. 5–1) will remain there for roughly a million years—just the time it takes to convert most of its hydrogen to helium, giving off energy in the process. Then much more quickly—perhaps in a hundred thousand years—it will move horizontally to the upper right region of the color-magnitude diagram. In doing so it will cross the cepheid region where it will

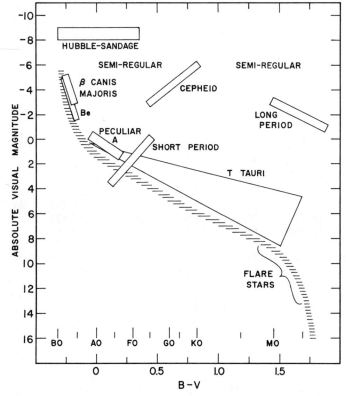

Figure 5–1. A color-magnitude diagram showing the Main Sequence (hatched strip) and various classes of intrinsic variables that are probably or certainly members of Baade's population I.

pulsate in a regular manner and with a light range of about one magnitude. Before and after this it will be pulsating very slightly in a semiregular manner. However the period of pulsation varies from about a day for stars near the Main Sequence to several years for stars in the upper right region. Therefore we would expect that during the thousand or ten thousand years that it takes for a star to cross the cepheid strip its period would increase by roughly 10 per cent.

Now it may seem impossible to detect a change in period from, say, ten to eleven days as it occurs gradually over ten thousand years. But periods of variable stars can be determined very accurately. Suppose that we can determine the time of maximum of this star to within 10 minutes (0.07 per cent of 10 days) and we have observations during 250 cycles. Then we should know its period at that time to within 0.0003 per cent. However a linear change of one day in ten thousand years amounts to 0.01 per cent change in ten years, which is much larger than our accuracy of 0.0003 per cent. Therefore it should be possible to detect evolutionary changes in variable stars in only ten years!

Cepheids do show period changes but these are not always increases in period and in some cases the changes are too fast. One cepheid (Swope 1937) seemed to have changed its period gradually from twelve to 21 days in just nine years. In other variables the period changes are sudden. We do not understand such changes. However cepheids are not observed well enough: most of the bright ones do not even have photoelectric light curves and the resulting accurate ephemerides. There are at least 360 known cepheids; the ones brighter than photographic magnitude 9.0 at all times are listed in Table 5–3, which has been abstracted from Kukarkin, *et. al.* (1958).

The pertinent observations for period changes could be made in one color and with nearby comparison stars. A dozen observations of each star during one night are sufficient. If the weather cooperates, the whole light curve of each star can be filled out in a couple months of scattered good nights. Summaries of older observations are given for the brighter variables by Schneller (1952, 1957, 1960) and Prager (1941), although these references are not readily available to most amateurs. However once some good observations are obtained most professional astronomers particularly interested in cepheids will be glad to assist in the literature search.

Table 5-3
Classical Cepheids Brighter Than 9.0 Photographic Magnitude At All Times

Star	α	δ	m_{ptg}		Ephemeris	
	(1960)		Max.	Min.	Epoch	Period
	h m	° ′				d
SU Cas	2 48.3	+68 43.6	6.21	6.78	2430404.134 +	1.949319 E
AW Per	4 45.1	+36 39.4	7.9	8.8	16512.64	6.46338
RX Aur	4 58.6	+39 54.3	8.0	9.0	30079.02	11.6248
β Dor	5 33.3	−62 31.9	4.5	5.7	26013.930	9.84235
T Mon	6 23.1	+ 7 6.7	6.40	7.96	32245.36	27.0205
RT Aur	6 26.0	+30 31.4	5.3	6.5	20957.466	3.728261
W Gem	6 32.7	+15 21.9	6.9	7.9	13266.65	7.91467
ζ Gem	7 1.7	+20 38.0	4.44	5.20	34426.65	10.15172
AP Pup	7 56.4	−40 0.8	7.9	8.8	27475.14	5.08431017
V Car	8 27.9	−59 59.3	8.0	8.7	21402.23	6.696734
RZ Vel	8 35.6	−43 58.3	7.04	8.5	34906.70	20.39652
V Vel	9 21.1	−55 47.3	7.65	8.75	34918.41	4.370991
I Car	9 44.1	−62 19.4	5.0	6.0	33233.30	35.556
Y Car	10 31.7	−60 17.5	8.25	8.8	34847.28	3.639760
VY Car	10 43.0	−57 21.2	7.58	8.7	34907.99	18.9349
U Car	10 56.2	−59 31.0	6.43	8.38	34528.22	38.7560
ER Car	11 8.0	−58 37.2	7.6	8.0	26777.62	7.717806
IT Car	11 10.5	−61 32.3	8.3	8.7	24214.92	7.5356
S Mus	12 10.6	−69 55.7	6.52	7.30	34580.62	9.65869
T Cru	12 19.1	−62 3.6	6.96	7.7	34534.47	6.73322
R Cru	12 21.4	−61 24.5	6.85	8.0	34922.31	5.82575
R Mus	12 39.6	−69 11.3	6.30	7.3	34847.38	7.50990
S Cru	12 52.0	−58 12.9	6.65	7.7	34931.23	4.690021
V Cen	14 29.7	−56 42.8	6.97	8.1	34869.61	5.49397
R TrA	15 16.0	−66 21.3	6.81	7.7	34920.49	3.389287
S TrA	15 57.5	−63 40.1	6.42	7.63	34575.42	6.32344
S Nor	16 15.5	−57 48.4	6.84	7.81	34586.39	9.76418
RV Sco	16 55.7	−33 33.1	7.22	8.4	34925.38	6.06133
BF Oph	17 3.6	−26 31.8	7.54	8.4	34941.08	4.06782
X Sgr	17 45.0	−27 49.2	4.8	5.8	19213.060	7.01266
W Sgr	18 2.5	−29 35.2	4.70	5.92	34587.26	7.594710
AP Sgr	18 10.6	−23 7.9	7.00	8.27	34907.39	5.057813
Y Sgr	18 19.0	−18 52.9	5.86	6.96	35364.22	5.77335
U Sgr	18 29.5	−19 29.5	7.02	8.16	16628.046	6.744925
V350 Sgr	18 42.9	−20 41.6	7.67	8.75	35358.43	5.15424
YZ Sgr	18 47.1	−16 46.3	7.77	8.87	34931.42	9.55345
BB Sgr	18 48.6	−20 20.8	7.36	8.2	35303.49	6.63699
FF Aql	18 56.5	+17 18.3	5.80	6.31	24703.115	4.470959
U Aql	19 27.2	− 7 7.8	6.79	7.95	34922.31	7.02393
SU Cyg	19 43.5	+29 9.9	6.8	7.66	33095.944	3.845664
η Aql	19 50.4	+ 0 54.0	4.08	5.25	32926.749	7.176641
S Sge	19 54.1	+16 31.6	5.87	7.02	33131.80	8.38216
X Cyg	20 41.7	+35 26.4	6.5	8.20	25739.90	16.3866
DT Cyg	21 4.8	+31 1.3	6.0	6.46	24305.124	2.49934
δ Cep	22 27.7	+58 12.6	4.1	5.2	2427628.86 +	5.366341 E

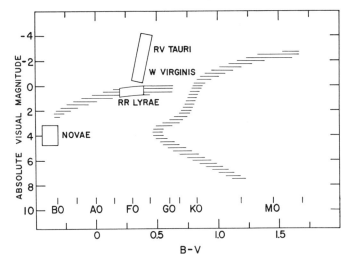

Figure 5–2. A color magnitude diagram for a typical globular cluster (hatched strips) and for various classes of population II variables. The relation between spectral types and colors is based on population I stars.

SEMIREGULAR VARIABLES

Most or all of the stars in the upper right part of the color-magnitude diagram are variable in a semiregular manner and with light ranges mostly between a tenth and one magnitude. Each cycle is not the same length as the others but almost all cycles are between $\frac{1}{2}$ and $1\frac{1}{2}$ times the average length. By following a star through roughly ten cycles one can obtain a fairly good average period.

Periods of semiregular stars are important because they lead to determinations of masses, and we have masses for only a couple stars in the whole upper right corner of the color-magnitude diagram. The period of a pulsating star is related to the average density throughout the star and to the pulsation constant, which is known approximately from theory. The average density, in turn, is obtained from the mass and radius of the star, and the radius is known if we know its distance and temperature. Therefore we can determine the masses of semi-regular stars in clusters or associations if we know their periods.

The observations of semiregular stars are not difficult to obtain. Again observations in one color are sufficient but not ideal. A good

Table 5-4
Known or Possible Semiregular Variables with Unknown Perods and in Clusters

Cluster or Association	Star	α		δ (1960)		Average m_v
		h		°	m	
NGC 457	BD+57°258	1	17.3	+58	5.7	8.6
I Persei	BD+58°273	1	37.6	+58	51.0	8.5
	HD 13136	2	6.6	+56	22	7.6
	BD+57°524	2	10.7	+57	58.2	8.9
	BU Per *	2	16.0	+57	14.3	9.2
	BD+58°445	2	15.6	+58	29.0	8.2
	FZ Per **	2	18.1	+56	58.6	8.0
	HD 14404	2	18.7	+57	40	7.8
	S Per	2	19.9	+58	24.4	9.0
	BD+56°595	2	20.3	+57	1.0	8.1
	HD 14580	2	20.5	+57	2	8.4
	HD 14826	2	22.5	+57	16	8.5
NGC 2439	CPD-31°1790	7	39.5	−31	35.2	8.2
I Gem	BU Gem **	6	9.9	+22	55.4	6.8
	WY Gem **	6	9.5	+23	13.2	9.5
δ Lyrae	δ² Lyrae	18	53.1	+36	50.7	4.4

magnitude determination once each week or two is sufficient because the periods are likely to be about a year. The principal difficulty is that the observer must be willing to stick with the project for at least several years or arrange with others to carry on when he is unable to do so himself.

A partial list of semiregular variables (or possible semiregulars) in clusters or associations but with unknown periods is given in Table 5–4. More such members are being found each year as more clusters are being studied.

SHORT PERIOD VARIABLES

The Short Period Variables (SPV) are a new (1957) class with not more than eleven known members at this writing. More will have to be found before we can delineate their characteristics. The best candidates are among the stars of spectral types A7 IV to F2 IV, where the *IV* denotes that they are brighter than Main Sequence stars. A list of such

* Period may be 365± days
** May be an irregular variable rather than a semiregular.

stars is given in Table 5–5. The light ranges are generally small (less than 0.1 mag.) so very accurate photometry will have to be carried out but the periods are conveniently short (1–5 hours). Most of the known SPV stars have secondary periods (Fitch 1959). A negative result on the variability of some stars in the color-magnitude diagram realm of the SPV stars may be just as important as a positive result.

Table 5-5
Possible Short Period Variables

Star	α	δ	m_v	Spectrum
		(1960)		
	h m	° ′		
β Cas	0 7.0	+58 56	2.4	F2 IV
χ Cet	1 47.6	−10 53	4.8	F2 IV
λ Ari	1 55.6	+23 24	4.8	F0 IV
HR 5110	13 32.6	+37 26	5.0	F2 IV
κ² Boo A	14 12.0	+51 59	4.6	A7 IV
16 Lib	14 55.1	− 4 11	4.6	F0 IV
δ Ser A	15 32.9	+10 40	4.2	F0 IV
HR 5960	15 56.8	+54 51	5.0	F0 IV
α Aql	19 23.5	+ 3 2	3.4	F0 IV
τ Cyg *	21 13.2	+37 52	3.8	F0 IV
ε Cep	22 13.6	+56 51	4.2	F0 IV
ζ¹ Aqr	22 26.3	− 0 17	4.6	F0 IV
ζ² Aqr			4.4	F0 IV
9 Lac	22 35.7	+51 20	4.8	A7 IV

NOVAE

Novae are fascinating stars to observe because not only do they show large changes in light and color but each star behaves in an individual fashion to some extent. Dr. Payne-Gaposchkin (1957) gives many light curves. The general character of the light variations can be determined sufficiently well with photographic or careful visual observations but the advent of photoelectric photometry leads to some possibilities that have not been fully exploited.

Dr. Merle Walker (1957) has found that after novae have returned to their original brightness (years after their outbursts) they usually fluctuate in brightness very rapidly. Typically the light range is about

* Period of 3^h25^m suggested by Paraskevoloulos (1921).

0.1 mag. with an interval of five minutes between light maxima. Reliable observations can be obtained only with excellent skies and equipment and other stars should be observed as controls.

We do not know at what time after the outburst the rapid fluctuations commence or how long they last. Perhaps they do not even exhibit these fluctuations continously. Novae should be observed from time to time after their outbursts to look for these fluctuations. Payne-Gaposchkin (1957) and Walker (1957) give lists of old novae, but these are often too faint for accurate photometry with small instruments.

During most of the course of an outburst of a novae most of the light comes from a few dozen strong emission lines, rather than from a continuous spectrum. Consequently the color is not simply related to the temperature of the star but rather to the excitation of certain emission lines from certain atoms. In other words, UBV colors are hard to use and interpret. Much more meaningful data would be the light curves of certain emission lines. These can be obtained with suitably selected interference filters. Spectra of novae are illustrated by Aller (1954a) and others. Also, do the rapid fluctuations found by Dr. Walker occur in each of the emission lines?

These are just a few samples of the large number of projects on intrinsic variable stars which can be done with small- or moderate-sized instruments and good photoelectric equipment in the hands of an enthusiastic and careful person whose knowledge of astrophysics is not large. When such a person has demonstrated his interest and persistence he can usually get the cooperative assistence of a professional astronomer who is a specialist in this field.

REFERENCES

Abt, H. A. 1957. *Ap. J.*, **126**: 138.
Aller, L. H. 1957a. *Astrophysics*, Vol. 2. New York: Ronald Press.
———. 1954b. *Pub. Dom. Ap. Obs.* **9**: 321.
Babcock, H. W. 1958. *Ap. J.* **128**: 228.
———. 1960. *Pub. Ast. Soc. Pacific.* **72**: 53.
Crawford, D. L. 1958. *Ap. J.* **128**: 185.
Deutsch, A. J. 1947. *Ap. J.* **105**: 283.
Eggen, O. J. 1951. *Ap. J.* **113**: 367.
———. 1957. *Nonstable Stars*. Cambridge: University Press.
Fitch, W. S. 1959. *Ap. J.* **130**: 1022.

Herbig, G. H. 1952. *J. Roy, Ast. Soc. Canada.* **46**: 222.
_____. 1957. *Nonstable Stars.* Cambridge. University Press.
Hubble, E., and Sandage, A. 1953. *Ap. J.* **118**: 353.
Kukarkin, B. V., Parengo, P. P., Efremov, Iu. I., and Kholopov, P. N. 1958. *The General Catalogue of Variable Stars*, Volumes I and II. Moscow: U.S.S.R. Academy of Sciences.
Joy, A. H. 1947, *Ap. J.* **105**: 96.
_____. 1949, *Ap. J.* **110**: 105.
_____. 1952, *Ap. J.* **115**: 25.
_____. 1954, *Pub. Ast. Soc. Pacific*, **66**: 5.
McNamara, D. H. and Hansen, K., 1961, *Ap. J.* **134**: 207.
Merril, P. W., and Burwell, C. G. 1949. *Ap. J.* **110**: 387.
Paraskevoloulos, J. S. 1921. *Ap. J.* **53**: 144.
Payne-Gaposchkin, C. 1951. *Astrophysics.* ed. J. A. Hynek. New York: McGraw-Hill. P. 517.
_____. 1957. *The Galactic Novae.* New York: Interscience.
Prager, R. 1941. *Harvard Annals*, Vol. 111.
Preston, G. W. 1959. *Ap. J.* **130**: 507.
Schneller, H. 1952, 1957, 1960. *Geschichte und Literatur des Lichtwechsels der Veränderlichen Sterne*, Vol. I-V. Berlin: Akademie Verlag.
Struve. O. 1955. *Pub. Ast. Soc. Pacific.* **67**: 135.
_____. 1959. *Sky and Telescope.* **18**: 612
Swope, H. H. 1937. *Harvard Annals.* **105**: 499.
Walker, M. F. 1957. *Nonstable Stars*, ed. G. H. Herbig. Cambridge: University Press. P. 46.

CHAPTER 6

Observation of

Eclipsing Variables

BY FRANK BRADSHAW WOOD

Flower and Cook Observatory, University of Pennsylvania

Amateur astronomers have tended to ignore eclipsing variable stars and to concentrate on intrinsic variables. However there is no reason why an amateur astronomer equipped with a simple photoelectric photometer mounted on a telescope of moderate size cannot make significant contributions to this field. Indeed the 1957 issue of the *Publications of the Astronomical Society of the Pacific* carries a complete light curve of the star u Her observed by an amateur astronomer, J. J. Ruiz, and other amateurs are currently carrying on observing programs on these stars. There are various ways in which an amateur can contribute, and his selection of a program will depend on his equipment, the time free for an observing program, and his personal inclination.

TIMES OF MINIMA

One extremely useful contribution would be the observations of the times of minimum light of selected eclipsing systems. These observations can serve two purposes. First, they will lead to an improved value of the period, and this is of particular usefulness to spectroscopists who will wish to compute accurately the phases of their own observations in order to plot a velocity curve. In the second place, for many eclipsing stars the periods do not remain constant, and a study of the nature of their changes is of considerable importance.

The variation in period can arise from various causes. In some systems the stars are moving in elliptical rather than circular orbits about the center of mass of the system. Because each component will be distorted from spherical shape by the attraction of the other, it can be shown that the direction in space in which the major axis of the ellipse is pointed will not remain constant, but will rotate very slowly. That is to say, at one time the orientation relative to the earth will appear as shown in Figure 6–1a while a number of years later the same two stars will be revolving in an orbit whose size and shape have not changed, but for which the orientation is now as shown in Figure 6–1b. For purposes of simplicity the "relative orbit" is shown in which one star is imagined to be stationary with the other moving about it.

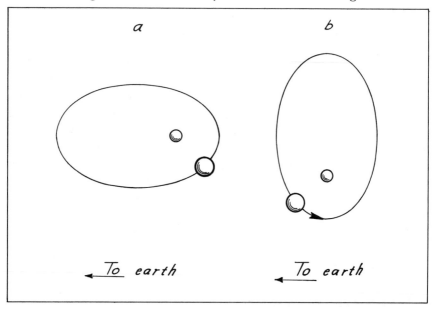

Figure 6–1.

There are two observational consequences of this "rotation of the line of apsides." Suppose the star represented as fixed is the hotter one, so that when it is eclipsed the deeper, or primary, minimum occurs. To obey the familiar law of areas, the cooler star will not move at constant speed, but will move most rapidly when it is closest to the hotter star. Thus when the orbit is oriented as in Figure 6–1a, the cooler star will be moving most slowly when it eclipses the other one, and the primary eclipse will last longer than the secondary which takes place half a period later. When the orientation is as in Figure 6–1b, the duration of the eclipses will be equal, but now secondary minimum will not occur exactly one-half period after primary. As shown by the diagram the distance in its orbit which the star will have to travel from primary to secondary is much shorter than the distance from the place of secondary to the next primary eclipse, and in addition the star will be traveling faster going from primary to secondary than in other parts of the orbit, because the stars are then closer together. The net result is that secondary minimum occurs before one-half the period has elapsed and is displaced forward on the light curve. When the orbit has rotated another 180°, exactly the reverse situation prevails, and more than a half period must elapse before secondary occurs. It can be shown that if we observe times of minimum light throughout a complete revolution of the orbit, the period as determined by observations of primary minimum will decrease and increase in a regular manner, and that as determined by secondary will do the same but will be lengthening, while that determined by the primary is shortening and vice versa. Thus by continued observations of minima we can determine how long it takes for one rotation of the entire orbit.

Now a knowledge of this length of line is more important than would at first appear. When we attempt to compute theoretically what this interval should be, we find that it depends among other things on the "models" on which the stars are constructed and in particular on how much the density increases in going from the surface to the center. This is of fundamental importance in our understanding of what is taking place deep in the stellar interiors, and hence any observational check is extremely valuable. Thus for these systems precise determination of times of minimum is a valuable contribution indeed. When secondary minimum is deep enough so that its time of minimum can be determined with precision, it should be observed also.

Most eclipsing systems have circular orbits and so are not useful for this particular purpose. However in many cases even these do not show constant periods. Frequently these changes are erratic and unpredictable. Sometimes a system which has had a constant period for years will show a sudden shift to a slightly longer or slightly shorter value; some systems never show constant periods for any length of time. We cannot say with certainty what the cause of these changes is, but it seems very likely indeed that it is connected with rapid ejection of material from at least one star of the system, analogous perhaps to prominence action on the sun. The dynamic conditions that exist because of the presence of the other star make it easier for such matter to escape than would otherwise be the case.

The difficulty in past work in most cases has been that because the period changes are small (usually of the order of a second or less) they cannot be detected until after some time has ellapsed. If a time of minimum can be determined with an accuracy of only fifteen minutes, for example, and a period variation of 0.1 second occurs, then 9,000 orbital revolutions of the stars must occur before the change can be detected, for this is the time it will take before the observed minima will vary by fifteen minutes from those predicted from the older value of the period. For a star with a three-day period, this means that nearly 75 years must ellapse. If during that interval another change occurs, the results of the two will be hopelessly intermingled. Today, we do not know in most cases whether we are observing the results of one or more large changes or the cumulative effect of a large number of small variations. Our only hope of getting better information is by the type of precise observations that can be made by the photoelectric method. Our chief hope of getting these soon for a significant number of systems lies in enthusiastic amateurs who will undertake this sort of work.

OBSERVATION AND REDUCTIONS

When the duration of eclipse is short enough, an entire minimum can be observed in a few hours. In this case the observations should preferably begin before or very shortly after loss of light has begun and continue for an equal interval after minimum light. Since the minima will not always occur at the times predicted from even the best light elements, a little leeway should be allowed. In the case of very deep minima, it is not absolutely necessary to cover the entire minimum if a period in which significant light changes occur is covered. The time of minimum light should, of course, come near the middle of the observing interval. If the star is to be observed for times of minimum only, there is no need to observe in more than one color. For a fairly bright star a blue filter is slightly preferable (for observations of primary minima), since the light loss generally will be greater in the blue than in the yellow, and the minimum can be determined more accurately. If the star is near the limit of faintness which can be reached, it may be advisable to use no filter at all, in order to increase the contrast between the readings on the star and the dark current. If sky background rather than dark current is the limiting factor, elimination of a filter usually offers no particular advantage. However if the star is reddish, use of a yellow filter may increase the ratio of star to sky. As in most observational work, good judgment by the observer is essential to a wise choice, and there is no substitute for experience.

In many cases the minima last so long that they cannot be covered in a few hours or even in an entire night. Systems of this type must be observed on two or more nights in order to obtain accurate times of minima. In most cases a run of two or three hours or longer should be made on each night, and it is desirable for the observations on each night to overlap in phase the observations of at least one other night.

For example, suppose a star takes fourteen hours to go through eclipse, but is high enough to be observed properly for only five hours (in general, observations below an altitude of 30° will not be satisfactory, although the exact limit depends on the quality of the sky). The observer may decide that six hours on either side of primary is sufficient to give an accurate time of minimum. On the first night he can observe, from, say, six hours before primary to one hour before, and get most of the descending branch of the light curve. If he is fortunate, perhaps the next time the star is in eclipse, he will be able to observe from three hours before until two hours afterward, and on a third night to start at one hour afterward and complete his observations. Needless to say, in most locations the weather probably will not cooperate, and the observer must be endowed with patience and even be prepared on occasion to wait until the next observing season to repeat his observations. This should be avoided when possible and the observations taken as closely together as is feasible.

The general observing technique in all variable star observation is to measure alternately the variable and a nearby comparison star of constant brightness. In Chapter 4 F. M. Bateson has described in detail a procedure particularly appropriate to astronomers using a meter to measure the amplifier output. Some amateurs may be fortunate enough to have an automatic recorder. The same general procedures apply, except that instead of taking several successive readings on a star, it is now better to record steadily for, say, one minute and then to go to the other star. As with the meter the usual sequence of events is C–V–C–V–C, etc., where C stands for a measure of the comparison star and V is a measure of the variable. The brightness of the sky background must also be measured at intervals. There is no fixed rule as to how frequently this must be done, and the ability to select the proper interval for a given night and star is part of the art of astronomical photometry learned only by experience. The suggestions made in Chapter 4 will serve as a good guide to the beginner. When the sky background becomes an appreciable part of the total deflection, naturally it is necessary to monitor the sky more frequently. Care should be taken to make certain that a faint star or bit of nebulosity is not included in the sky readings.

Sometime during the night it is advisable to substitute a check star for one of the variable star readings as a guard against inconstant light in the supposedly steady comparison star. Ideally this should be done in the beginning of the evening and again at the end.

If the light of the variable is changing very rapidly and the transparency is extremely steady, sometimes two or three measures of the variable can be taken between successive comparison star readings. It is absolutely necessary to record the time of every observation of the variable star; the mean time of the observation can be determined if the time at which the deflection reaches full scale is recorded and the time of ending the observation is likewise noted. In almost every case, times recorded to the nearest 0.1 minute are sufficient. It is, of course, assumed that the observer checks his watch by radio time signals or other reliable means before beginning observations and again after their conclusion. The hour angle of variable and comparison star should be noted during each observation.

Now let us suppose that the observer has completed his night's work and wishes to determine a time of minimum. First, the observations must be "reduced". Usually this means determining from the tracings the difference of magnitude between the variable and the comparison star at each instant when a variable star measure was made.

First to be treated are the times of the observations. Each time is expressed in Julian days and decimals of a day. The table giving the Julian day for the first day of each year from 1900 to 2009 is presented in the appendix. Mechanically inclined observers who wish to spare themselves the arithmetic of computing decimals of a day may find it worthwhile to construct a clock which reads decimals of a day directly. A simple but effective model has been described in *Sky and Telescope*, Vol. 10, p. 226. The only materials required are one rpm motor, two simple gears, and a simple counter. This clock can be preset to Greenwich time if desired and the heliocentric correction for the night applied in advance, so that no alterations need be made to the recorded times. The final step (unless it has been applied in advance) is the application of heliocentric corrections. The means of computing Julian days and the heliocentric corrections have been described in Chapter 4.

Now the magnitude differences between variable and comparison must be derived from the tracings. (It is, of course, permissible to work in intensity ratios instead, but most astronomers soon develop a preference for working in magnitudes, and the logarithmic scale offers definite advantages in deep eclipses. The method of doing this has also been described in Chapter 4, and only minor differences of procedure are followed by an observer using an automatic recorder. For example, instead of plotting the sky sets, lines can be drawn between them as illustrated in Figure 6–2 in order to find the proper value of the sky reading at the time of each star measure.

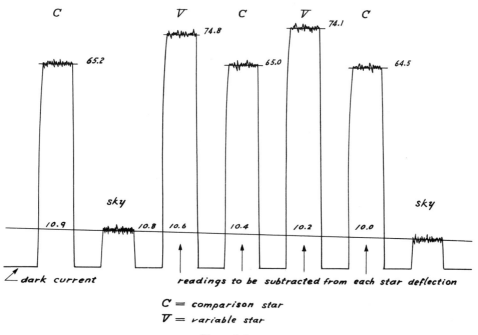

Figure 6–2.

A sample reduction of this tracing is shown. A four-place table of logarithms to the base 10 is needed. The fundamental relation between difference of magnitude and intensity ratio is:

$$m_1 - m_2 = 2.5 \log L_2/L_1 = 2.5 (\log L_2 - \log L_1).$$

A sample reduction of the above tracing is as follows:

$$
\begin{aligned}
(\text{comparison} - \text{sky})_1 &= 65.2 - 10.9 = 54.3 \\
(\text{variable} - \text{sky})_2 &= 74.8 - 10.6 = 64.2 \\
(\text{comparison} - \text{sky})_2 &= 65.0 - 10.4 = 54.6 \\
(\text{variable} - \text{sky})_2 &= 74.1 - 10.2 = 63.9 \\
(\text{comparison} - \text{sky})_3 &= 64.5 - 10.0 = 54.5
\end{aligned}
$$

Thus we have:

variable (1) = 64.2	variable (2) = 63.9
mean comparison (1,2) = 54.45	mean comparison (2,3) = 54.55

log 64.2 = 1.8075	log 63.9 = 1.8055
log 54.45 = 1.7360	log 54.55 = 1.7368
difference 0.0715	difference 0.0687

$$(\Delta m)_1 = 2.5 \times 0.0715 = 0.179 \overset{m}{} \qquad (\Delta m)_2 = 2.5 \times 0.0687 = 0.172 \overset{m}{}$$

For those not familiar with logarithms, an alterate method of reduction is to take the ratio of the intensities, always dividing the smaller deflection by the larger, and then to read the difference of magnitude directly from Table 2 in the appendix. In the example just given, we would have:

$$
\begin{aligned}
(I_c/I_v)_1 &= 54.45/64.2 = 0.8481 \\
(I_c/I_v)_2 &= 54.55/63.9 = 0.8537
\end{aligned}
$$

Entering Table 2 with these intensity ratios, we find $(\Delta m)_1 = 0.179$ and $(\Delta m)_2 = 0.172$, as before.

These m's must then be adjusted for differential extinction between variable and comparison star by the method described in Chapter 4.

By this means the observations will be in the form of a table giving the corrected difference of magnitude for the various heliocentric times of observation of the variable. Such a table would appear as follows:

Table 6-1

GO Cygni. Hel. Universal Time	Blue filter Δm (C − V)	27 June, 1960 = JD 243 7113 Hel. Universal Time	Δm (C − V)
	m		m
JD 243 7117.5002	+0.468	JD 243 7104.5328	+0.428
.5056	.466	.5378	.426
.5112	.449	.5433	.419
.5168	.452	.5488	.407
.5219	.438	.5539	.406
.5274	+ .436	.5590	.399

The next step will be to derive from these observations a time of minimum light. Various methods have been devised to do this. Some of these, such as that of Hertzsprung or that of van Woerden and Kwee, probably involve too much mathematics to be interest to the average amateur. These are described in the *Bulletin of the Astronomical Institutes of the Netherlands*. If only one minimum has been observed and the observations have all been made on one night, the simplest approach is merely to plot the magnitudes in the above table against time. A freehand curve through the observations often will give a satisfactory time of light minimum. If the curve is put on tracing paper, it can be shifted horizontally in time over the plotted observations in order to find how precisely the time of minimum is determined. In all cases an idea of the precision with which the minimum is determined should be given. If the curve is symmetrical, an alternate method is to draw lines connecting various points of equal brightness on the descending and ascending branches. The midpoints of each line will give a value for the minimum light and averages of various lines can be taken as the best value.

If the star has been observed on more than one night, and especially if the minimum was not completely covered on any one night, an alternate method is used. The predicted time of minimum nearest the time at which the observations were taken must be computed. In general this already will have been done in order to determine when to observe the star. Two methods are available. The Cracow Observatory issues annually a publication entitled *Supplemento Internationale* which contains predicted times of minimum for a very large number of eclipsing stars. (Requests for the publication should be addressed to Cracow Observatory, Jagellonian University, Cracow, Poland.) As an alternate, the astronomer may prefer to compute the predicted times of minimum for himself using the most recent "light elements."

These light elements consist of two quantities. One is the initial epoch, or some particular time when the star was at minimum light. The other is the period of light variation. Obviously by adding the period to the initial epoch a sufficient number of times, we can predict the light minimum which will fall nearest the date of observation. Then, from the observed times, we can compute the "phases" or intervals of time before or after the computed minimum.

As an example, in the case of GO Cygni, a set of light elements has been determined as:

$$\text{Primary minimum} = \text{JD } 2424509.461 + 0.7177632 \text{ E}$$

Here E can be any whole number of periods. If we multiply the period by 14,774 (the number of revolutions which have elapsed between the initial epoch and our assumed date of observation of 27 June, 1960 = JD 243 7113, and add this to the initial epoch, we find a predicted time of minimum at JD 243 7113.6945. Since Julian days begin at noon, this corresponds to approximately 4:40 A.M. on June 28, Greenwich time, or for an observer in the Eastern Standard time zone of the United States, 11:40 P.M. on the night of June 27. Observers of variable stars will find it convenient to begin reckoning their times and dates at noon; thus 1:00 A.M. simply becomes 1300 and the confusion of changing dates in the middle of an observing period is avoided.

Table 6-2

UT	Phase	Δm	UT	Phase	Δm
	d	m		d	m
7113.5002	−0.1943	+0.468	7113.5328	−0.1617	+0.428
.5056	− .1889	.466	.5378	− .1567	.426
.5112	− .1833	.449	.5433	− .1512	.419
.5168	− .1777	.452	.5488	− .1457	.407
.5219	− .1726	.438	.5539	− .1406	.406
.5274	− .1671	+ .436	.5590	− .1355	+ .399

If we consider the listed observations in Table 6–1, we can now compute phases from the predicted time of minimum of 243 7113.6945.

The negative sign indicates the observations were made before the minimum occurred; observations following minimum would bear a positive sign.

Now the observations of many nights can be plotted on the same diagram merely by plotting Δm against phase, and an idea of the shape of the minimum can be obtained. A freehand curve through the combined observations will indicate where the minium light occurs. If the minimum is symmetrical an independent determination of the point of minimum light can be made by bisecting lines joining points of equal brightness on the two branches as just described. Tracing paper should be placed over the observations and the curve and point of minimum light drawn on it. Next, the observations on any given night should be plotted as difference of magnitude against heliocentric time. The tracing paper is placed over this, with the magnitudes on the paper corresponding to those on the plot, and adjusted by moving horizontally (in time) until the best fit is obtained. The time corresponding to the point of minimum light on the curve is then the observed time of minimum for that night. The observer can also get an indication of the precision with which this is determined by seeing how much he can move the tracing paper horizontally before the fit of the curve to the observations becomes unsatisfactory.

An alternative method, devised by Dr. K. Kordylewski and described by Dr. Rosa Szafraniec of the Cracow Observatory (in Vol. 4, Series c of *Acta Astronomica*) is as follows:

The observations on any given night are plotted as difference of magnitude against heliocentric time; the scales are chosen so that the slope during the steepest phases of light loss or light gain is approximately 45°. As before, the observations and the coordinate system are transferred to tracing paper. The tracing paper is then turned over and, keeping the axes of the abcissae upon each other, placed so that the observations of the first branch drawn on the tracing paper fit those of the second branch on the original plot, and vice versa. Shifting the tracing paper to the right or left (but not vertically) we can find the best fit. The moment of minimum may then be found by taking the mean of the time on the tracing paper and that on the original plot, either for the minimum itself or any two points of equal magnitude (if the minimum is symmetrical). Shifting the tracing paper to the left and the right also gives the limits of precision. If observations are made on more than one night, phases must be plotted instead of time. The method is particularly useful when the observations are not numerous.

The final table the astronomer should prepare will contain the observed heliocentric times of minimum expressed in Julian days and decimals of a day, the epoch based on the light elements used, and the value of "$O - C$" (the difference between the observed and computed times of minimum). A hypothetical sample is shown in Table 6–3.

Table 6-1
GO Cygni: Primary minimum = 242 6509.461 + 0.7177632   E

Obs. Min.	Epoch	O–C
		d
JD 243 7113.698	14,774	+0.004
7115.853	14,777	+ .005
7121.594	14,785	+ .004
7123.749	14,788	+ .006

Further study for detecting variation of the period or finding improved light elements in general will be possible only if the amateur has access to an astronomical library where the older published observations are available.

A final question which will occur to some amateurs is how to find the latest light elements for any given system. These are published in the various catalogues of variable stars; that from Cracow is revised annually. If these are not available and if the observer has no access to a professional library, this information will be supplied on request from the Card Catalogue of Eclipsing Variables kept at the Flower and Cook Observatory of the University of Pennsylvania (Philadelphia 4, Pennsylvania). Amateurs in eastern Europe may prefer to request similar information from the Cracow Observatory, Cracow, Poland.

LIGHT CURVES

Much more information concerning the nature of an eclipsing system can be gained if the entire light curve is observed. This, combined with spectrographic observations, gives measures of such fundamental properties as masses, radii, and densities. Other effects which can be studied include those resulting from the distortion of each star from spherical shape and the effects caused by the radiation of each star on the adjacent side of the other. The detailed analysis of a light curve is not an easy problem, and probably many amateurs will not care to undertake it. However, especially for a preliminary solution, the mathematics required will not exceed that needed for a bachelor's degree in engineering or the sciences. For those interested, details will be found in Chapter 7. In any case, if a good light curve has been observed, it will probably be easy to find astronomers specializing in the field who will be eager to carry out the analysis.

There is also another reason for observing light curves. As precise observations continue to be made, it is becoming increasingly clear that most (if not all) eclipsing systems have "complications" in their light curves—that is, effects not clearly explained by the conventional theoretical treatment. These cause the light curves to differ from season to season, or sometimes during one observing season. Some of these effects are probably caused by shells or streams of gas around the stars; others may be due to dark areas of the photosphere similar to sunspots. Future progress in our knowledge will depend in part on having for each system a number of light curves observed at different epochs.

The general observing procedure will be similar to that just described, but certain details need emphasis. First, it is extremely important to select a "check" star and to observe it at least once every night observations are made. Since we never actually observe the magnitude of the variable star, but rather observe the difference of magnitude between it and the comparison star, it is important to be certain that any changes reported are really changes in the variable and not changes in the star with which it is being compared. The time spent in comparing this comparison star with another in order to be certain of its constancy is time well spent.

The observations will be of considerably more value if they are made in two or three spectral regions outlined by appropriate filters, as discussed in Chapter 3. The precise technique may vary from star to star. If the deflections are of the same order of magnitude in all wavelengths, and if the light changes are relatively slow, it may be practicable to observe the comparison star in three colors successively, then the variable in three colors, the comparison again, and so forth, taking sky observations as often as necessary. If the equipment is so constructed that it is possible to go rapidly from star to sky and back to star, it is probably better to observe in this sequence: star with filter No. 1, sky with filter No. 1, star with filter No. 2, sky with filter No. 2, star with filter No. 3, sky with filter No. 3. However if appreciable time is lost in recentering, it is wiser to observe the star in all three colors and then go to the sky. Only experience and judgment can decide.

Sometimes the deflection in one color is so much less than in the others that an entirely different "gain" on the amplifier must be used. In this case, or when the light changes are quite rapid, it is advisable to observe in only two colors. Even so, it is useful to take measures in all three at selected points on the light curve. Measurements near the center of secondary, for example, give a color which usually is very close to that of the primary component. If primary minimum represents a total eclipse, measures during totality will give the color of the secondary component.

It is advisable to reduce and to plot the observations as promptly as possible. Phases are computed as described before, and the plot of magnitude difference against phase constitutes the light curve. Just when the curve can be said to be completed is a matter of judgment. Both minima should be thoroughly covered with observations in each made in general on at least three nights. The light curve between minima should also be covered at least twice if possible. This is needed not only for the "rectification" of the observations—the first step in the solution—but also to detect complications in the curve. The comparison-check star magnitude differences (corrected for differential extinction) should also be computed. Parts of the curve which frequently are not observed sufficiently are the "shoulders," or those parts of the minima where the eclipses are just beginning or just ending. The portions of the curve just outside eclipse are important both for the rectification and also in determining depths of eclipses and every effort should be made to cover them adequately.

Measurement of Comparison Stars

There is yet another type of observational program which can prove useful: the study of the other stars near the variable which might prove suitable comparison stars. This study can be carried out by astronomers who wish to devote only a limited part of their time to eclipsing stars or who cannot spare the time to make the relatively long runs usually needed for completing minima or observing complete light curves. It may also be done by an observer as preliminary to a thorough study of a particular variable. The purpose in either case is to measure the brightness and color of nearby stars which might be selected as comparison stars and to be as certain as possible that these stars are not themselves variable.

The choice of a suitable comparison star is an extremely important item in the observing program, and neglect of the proper precautions may make virtually useless many long nights of observing. The astronomer should always bear in mind that what he is measuring is the difference of magnitude between variable and comparison stars, and any uncertainty in the constancy of the comparison will cause a corresponding lack of confidence in the reliability of the observed light curve. Despite his eagerness to start his programs, he should be as certain as possible that the comparison star used is constant in brightness—or, perhaps to be absolutely precise we should say that its variations in brightness are less than can be detected by existing techniques. As stated in Chapter 4, the ideal comparison star should satisfy various criteria. Frequently it will not be possible to find one which satisfies all of these, and the "best" in any particular case will often be a matter of judgment. Ideally it should be quite close in sky to the variable star. When practical it is wise to choose a comparison within half a degree of the variable, although especially with the brighter stars this is frequently not possible. Obviously the closer the comparison star, the less important will be uncertainties in knowledge of the precise value of the extinction coefficient. Further, the time in going from comparison to variable will be reduced. Not only will this permit more observations per unit of time, but also the precision will be somewhat increased since transparency variations will be more accurately measured by the increased frequency of comparison star measures. For many telescopes it will help if the comparison star is nearly the same right ascension or nearly the same declination as the variable. For example, if the observer, after observing the comparison star, can unclamp the telescope in declination only and move it until he sees the variable nearly centered in the field, he can save a great deal of time as contrasted to the case where he has to move to the proper position as nearly as it can be determined from the declination circle, and then clamp the declination and repeat the process in right ascension, and then find and center the star.

It has been remarked that photoelectric photometry is at its best when comparing the sources of early equal brightness. In such a case, any nonlinearity of the amplifier becomes of little importance, and the gain can be adjusted to give deflections of the most convenient size. Thus another, and more important, criterion is that the comparison star should have approximately the same magnitude as the variable. Obviously, except for systems with very small amplitudes, this criterion is impossible to satisfy because of the changes in brightness of the variable. The best solution is again a matter of judgment, and may vary from case to case depending on the available stars in the neighborhood of the variable. Since variations in the sky brightness (as distinct from variations in extinction) will be less important the greater the difference between readings on the sky alone and readings on star plus sky, a case can be made for choosing the comparison star about the same brightness as the variable at maximum light. Another procedure is to choose a comparison star somewhat fainter then the variable at maximum to decrease the magnitude difference between the two when the variable is at minimum. The exact choice in each case may well be dictated by the stars in neighborhood of the variable, but every effort should be made to select a comparison star which is neither considerably brighter than the variable at maximum nor appreciably fainter than the variable at minimum. An alternative procedure, which is not recommended, is the use of two or more comparison stars. This procedure is frequently followed in making photographic and visual estimates, and indeed with these techniques it can scarcely be avoided. However the linearity of the photosensitive surface makes it possible to work with only one comparison star over a considerable range of intensity variations and thus to avoid the various sources of error introduced by using several comparison stars.

Finally, it is extremely important that the comparison star have nearly the same color as the variable. Again, this may be a difficult criterion to fulfil. Except in the case of W Ursae Majoris systems or others having similar spectra, or in cases of relatively shallow eclipses, the color of the variable will change considerably, especially during the primary eclipse. Particularly troublesome are cases like zeta Aurigae, in which one component of the eclipsing system is a star of spectral class B and the other is a much larger star of spectral class K. In this case the B star predominates in the shorter wavelength regions and the K star in the longer. The exact distribution of energy in the spectrum will be complex, and it will not be possible to duplicate it with any single star. Such systems are relatively few, and it usually will be possible to ascertain what comparison stars have been used in earlier works and to continue to use these. Use of these comparison stars has an additional advantage of making it easier to compare various sets of observational data.

Specific Observing Programs.

There is a certain amount of danger in recommending specific observing programs, partly because the selection of a program is a matter of judgment dictated by the interests of the observer who will spend his time making the measures. More seriously, it is true because of the many rapid changes in the field. Twenty years ago, for example, we tended to think that almost all light curves remainded constant, cycle after cycle and year after year. Thus if a light curve had been thoroughly covered by a series of precise observations and a solution for elements made, there was a tendency to label the solution "definitive" and to think that there was no particular need of repeating observation of the light curve unless it could be done with greater precision or in a different color. Today we know that many systems—possibly all systems—show changes not explicable by the eclipse theory itself, and these "complications" are often different at different epochs. Thus almost any system will repay observation, provided the observations are sufficiently accurate and are free from systematic errors. However observations of some systems may be expected to add significantly more to our knowledge than equal time spent in observing others, and a few remarks concerning this may be in order.

In general the shorter the period, the easier it is to obtain a complete light curve. In the case of W UMa systems, it is possible to cover an entire light curve in one or two nights observing, and a series of three or four clear nights in a row will give a very satisfactory coverage. In many parts of the world the general weather pattern is a series of clear nights followed by a number of cloudy ones, and thus it is possible to collect a series of light curves for a given star. Each light curve will be composed of observations made on a few closely grouped dates. Comparison of these will enable us to study in some detail the changes taking place in the curves, leading eventually to a better understanding of the causes of these changes. Except in extremely favorable climates, the observer will probably be wise to limit himself to one system at any particular observing season and to concentrate on that.

In contrast, systems with longer periods have been neglected some-what, and in general the longer the period, the greater the neglect. The reason for this is easy to understand. An appreciable amount of the literature concerning eclipsing stars has been contributed by graduate students working on doctoral dissertations; another significant fraction has come from astronomers who obtained their observational material while on visits to observatories in better climates. In either case time usually did not permit the study of systems with longer periods. Even in the case of astronomers working at their own institu-tions there is a natural desire to complete a curve as soon as possible, and hence a tendency to avoid systems of long periods. Yet information of considerable importance can be obtained only from studies of these systems. For example, we would welcome accurate values for the masses of giant stars of the later spectral types. Yet the very size of these means that when found in eclipsing systems the periods must be long, ranging roughly from thirty days to many years. An observer willing to undertake a long-range program might well include several of these. Except for nights when the system is actually in eclipse, five or six observations in each color on a given night (together with check star measures) will usually be sufficient, and an observer can carry a number of such systems on his program.

Systems no fainter than tenth magnitude at minimum and having long periods are listed in Table 6–4. Several of these are known to be or are suspected of being intrinsically variable, so check star measure-ments on each night are essential.

The extreme cases of long-period, eclipsing stars are shown by epsilon and zeta Aurigae, 31 and 32 Cygni, VV Cephei, and V777 Sgr. In these, years elapse between eclipses, and the observed depths of eclipse depend strongly on the wave length in which the observations are made. At the time of each eclipse the systems are observed inten-sively, but usually very few photoelectric observations are taken in the intervals between. Most of these systems show intrinsic fluctuations. When these are superimposed on eclipse effects, it is extremely difficult to interpret the observations. A long series of photoelectric observa-tions between eclipses would be of great value in obtaining a better understanding of these peculiar systems. Again, five or six measures in each color and check star measures will usually be sufficient for

Table 6-4
Eclipsing Systems Having Long Periods

Name		R.A. (1900)	Dec.	Max	Pri. Min	Sec. Min	Per- iod	Eclipse duration
		h m	° ′	m	m	m	d	d
RR	Ari	01 50.3	+23 5	6.4	6.8	6.7	48	4
SX	Cas	00 05.5	+54 20	9.0	10.0	9.3	37	3.7
BM	Cas	00 48.6	+63 32	9.0	9.3	9.1	197	50
RX	Cas	02 58.8	+67 11	8.5	9.3	8.9	32	5
RZ	Cnc	08 32.9	+32 9	8.5	10.1	8.8	22	2.4
TW	Cnc	08 24.5	+12 47	9.0	10.0		71	1.1
UU	Cnc	07 56.9	+15 27	8.5	9.0	8.8	98	
W	Cru	12 06.7	−58 14	9.0	9.6	9.3	199	67
RZ	Eri	04 39.0	−10 53	8.0	9.2	8.2	39	2.2
AR	Mon	07 15.9	− 5 4	9.0	9.8	9.3	21	3.0
W	Ser	18 04.1	−15 34	9.0	9.9		14	
μ	Sgr	18 07.8	−21 5	4.0	4.1		180	
ν	Sgr	19 16.0	−16 9	4.3	4.5	4.5	138	
ε	UMi	16 56.2	+82 12	5.0	5.1		39	
AL	Vel	08 28.0	−47 20	9.0	10.3		96	8.4
ε	Aur	04 54.8	+43 40	3.5	4.3		9883	754
ζ	Aur	04 55.5	+40 56	5.0	5.5		972	39
VV	Cep	21 53.8	+63 9	6.5	7.3		7430	490
31	Cyg	20 10.5	+46 26	4.0	4.4		3800	67
32	Cyg	20 12.4	+47 24	4.2	4.4		1141	28
V777	Sgr	17 40.2	−26 9	9.4	9.7		936	56

the night's work. However, in VV Cephei (and possibly in others) the observer should be alert for relatively rapid (of the order of thirty minutes) increases of light which have occasionally been reported. Such increases can amount to several hundredths of a magnitude and are usually larger in the shorter wavelength regions.

An observer wishing to study times of minimum will have a wide choice of programs. One useful program could include repeated studies of systems showing irregular period fluctuations in an attempt to find more about the details of such changes. Other useful results might be found in connection with systems in which we anticipate rotation of the line of apsides. A number of systems have shown light curves with displaced secondaries indicating eccentric orbits, but apsidal motion as determined by studies of period changes has not yet been confirmed. In other cases spectrographic work has indicated eccentric orbits, but again measured times of minima have not yet shown apsidal motion.

Table 6-5
Systems for which Eccentric Orbits or
Displaced Secondary Minima Have Been Reported

Name		R.A. (1900)	Dec.	Max	Pri. Min	Sec. Min	Per- iod	Eclipse duration
		h m	° ′	m	m	m	d	h
TW	And	23 58.2	+32 17	9.0	11.0	9.2	4.12	13
XZ	And	01 50.8	+41 36	9.5	11.7	9.7	1.36	6
QS	Aql	19 36.5	+13 35	5.8	5.9	5.9	2.51	11
V805	Aql	19 00.7	−11 48	7.8	8.4	8.1	2.41	5
V889	Aql	19 12.3	+15 59	8.7	9.3		11.12	
RR	Ari	01 50.3	+23 5	6.4	6.8	6.7	47.9	48
TT	Aur	05 02.8	+39 27	8.5	9.6	9.1	1.33	8
EO	Aur	05 11.6	+36 31	7.5	7.8	7.6	4.07	22
RX	Cas	02 58.8	+67 11	8.5	9.3	8.9	32.32	120
YZ	Cas	00 39.2	+74 26	5.5	5.9	5.6	4.47	8
CC	Cas	03 06.2	+59 11	7.0	7.1	7.1	3.37	
SV	Cen	11 43.1	−60 1	9.0	10.2	9.6	1.66	
V350	Cen	11 45.3	−63 6	10.5	11.0		3.21	
V380	Cen	13 20.8	−61 21	9.5	10.1	9.8	1.09	4
V495	Cen	12 55.6	−55 33	10.4	11.9	10.6	33.49	106
XX	Cep	23 33.7	+63 47	8.5	9.5	9.6	2.34	8
AH	Cep	22 44.3	+64 32	7.0	7.2	7.2	1.77	7
CW	Cep	23 00.0	+62 51	7.6	8.0	7.9	2.73	8
SW	CMa	07 04.0	−22 17	9.0	9.5		10.09	12
α	CrB	15 30.4	+27 3	2.5	2.6		17.36	13
U	CrB	15 14.1	+32 1	7.5	8.6	7.7	3.45	10
W	Cru	12 06.7	−58 14	9.0	9.6	9.3	198.5	
RS	CVn	13 06.0	+36 28	8.0	9.2		4.80	12
SW	Cyg	20 03.8	+46 0	9.5	12.1		4.57	12
MR	Cyg	21 55.1	+47 30	8.5	9.3	8.7	1.68	8
V380	Cyg	19 47.2	+40 21	5.7	5.8	5.8	12.43	33
V382	Cyg	20 15.0	+36 0	8.5	9.3	9.2	1.89	
V448	Cyg	20 02.4	+35 7	8.0	8.5	8.3	6.52	15
V453	Cyg	20 02.8	+35 27	8.0	8.3	8.3	3.89	11
V470	Cyg	20 15.8	+40 34	8.7	8.8	8.8	1.87	
V477	Cyg	20 01.6	+31 42	8.5	9.4	8.7	2.35	4
W	Del	20 33.1	+17 56	9.5	12.2		4.81	14
TW	Dra	15 32.4	+64 14	7.5	9.8	7.6	2.81	9
RZ	Eri	04 39.0	−10 53	8.0	9.2	8.2	32.29	53
u	Her	17 13.6	+33 12	4.5	5.2	4.7	2.05	10
RX	Her	18 26.0	+12 32	7.0	7.6	7.5	1.78	6
UX	Her	17 49.7	+16 58	9.0	9.8	9.1	1.55	6
DI	Her	18 49.3	+24 9	8.0	8.8	8.6	10.55	8

Table 6-5 (continued)

Name		R.A. (1900)	Dec.	Max	Pri-Min	Sec.Min	Period	Eclipse duration
		h m	° ′	m	m	m	d	h
SX	Hya	13 39.0	−26 23	8.5	12.5		2.90	8
AI	Hya	08 13.6	+00 36	9.0	9.5	9.4	8.29	24
UV	Leo	10 33.0	+14 47	8.5	9.1	9.0	0.60	2
RR	Lyn	06 18.0	+56 20	5.5	5.9	5.7	9.94	10
TU	Mon	07 48.3	−02 47	8.5	10.9	8.6	5.05	18
AR	Mon	07 15.9	−05 4	9.0	9.8	9.3	21.21	71
AU	Mon	06 49.8	−01 15	8.5	9.4	8.6	11.11	24
FW	Mon	07 52.7	−06 55	9.4	10.6	9.4	3.87	12
IM	Mon	06 18.0	−03 14	6.5	6.6	6.6	1.19	
U	Oph	17 11.4	+01 19	5.5	6.2	6.1	1.68	6
V451	Oph	18 24.5	+10 50	7.9	8.5	8.3	1.10	5
BM	Ori	05 30.3	−05 27	8.0	8.7		6.47	17
EY	Ori	05 26.4	−05 47	9.5	10.3	9.6	16.79	31
AT	Peg	22 08.4	+07 56	8.5	9.3	8.7	1.15	5
EE	Peg	21 35.1	+08 44	7.0	7.6	7.1	2.63	8
ζ	Phe	01 04.2	−55 47	4.0	4.5	4.3	1.67	5
Y	Psc	23 29.3	+07 22	9.0	12.0		3.77	11
UU	Psc	00 09.8	+08 16	6.0	6.1	6.1	0.84	4
TY	Pup	07 28.4	−20 34	8.5	8.9	8.9	0.58	
μ¹	Sco	16 45.1	−37 52	3.0	3.3	3.2	1.45	
V453	Sco	17 49.7	−32 21	6.5	6.9	6.9	12.00	
RY	Sct	18 19.9	−12 45	9.5	10.0	10.0	11.12	
μ	Sgr	18 07.8	−21 5	4.0	4.1		180.4	480
RS	Sgr	18 11.0	−34 8	6.0	6.7	6.2	2.42	6
XZ	Sgr	18 15.9	−25 17	8.5	11.3		3.28	7
V1647	Sgr	17 52.4	−36 55	7.0	7.1	7.1	3.28	5
UY	Vir	12 56.6	−19 15	8.0	8.8		1.99	9
RS	Vul	19 13.4	+22 16	7.0	8.0	7.1	4.48	15

In still other systems apsidal motion has been detected, but a precise value of the period of this motion has not been found. A systematic program of measuring times of minima of any of these systems would be a worthwhile contribution. Table 6–5 lists a number of such systems; the list has been confined to those brighter than tenth magnitude of maximum.

In some of these it may be found that the reported eccentricities are spurious because of the distortion of the spectral lines by circumstellar gas streams. In others the reports of displaced secondaries may not be comfirmed by precise observations, or the apparent displacement may be due to asymmetry in the light curve. In still others it may prove extremely difficult to separate period changes caused by the rotation of the line of apsides from changes due to other causes. But most certainly from this list we can find some systems in which rotation of the apse can be measured.

CONCLUSION

In summary, the amateur interested in making photoelectric observations of eclipsing systems will have a choice of several types of program, not necessarily mutually exclusive, and a wide range of choice within each program. Two precautions should be mentioned. The first is against undertaking too ambitious a program. It is much better to observe one light curve thoroughly than to have fragments of six or seven. The second is that this is a rapidly changing field. Especially if he does not have access to the professional literature, the amateur would be well advised to write to one of the observatories working on this field before deciding definitely on his program.

CHAPTER 7

Observe, Then Preserve

BY JOHN E. MERRILL

Franklin Institute Research Laboratories

PART I

There is value, as well as pleasure, for the endividual in the "sight-seeing" or "tourist" type of observing. There is even more value for more people, as well as deep-seated satisfaction for the individual, in variable-star observations obtained as a part of a large-scale effort and then made available to other workers in the field.

Of the several centers at which such observations are collated and recorded for later use, one of the most widely known is the American Association of Variable Star Observers, the "AAVSO," with headquarters at 4 Brattle Street, Cambridge, Massachusetts. Many local or national societies maintain their own files of observations of variable stars; most such societies, recognizing the value of centralized recording, also communicate their lists to the AAVSO. Observations come in from the Asociacion Chilena de Astronomia to the south and from the Nordisk Astronomisk Selskab to the north, from the Variable Star Observers of Japan to the west and from the Berliner Arbeitsgemeinschaft für Veränderliche Sterne to the east; in her *Annual Report* for 1959 Mrs. Mayall said, "Observations were received from 184 observers in 18 countries."

Is this material "received and filed," relegated to a drawer marked "SS Cygni" or "Miscellaneous," and simply entered as "Number of Observations" in a report? One who looks at the monumental *Studies of Long-Period Variables*, published by Leon Campbell and Mrs. Mayall in 1955, sees a mine of information ready for use by professional astronomers in testing theories of structure, pulsation, and stellar evolution. In the *Astrophysical Journal* for March 1960, Dr. Paul W. Merrill (probably the world's foremost authority on cool, red stars) remarks that he has made, for his use in his article in Volume VI of Dr. Kuiper's encyclopedic series, a statistical study based on 360 long-period variables from the AAVSO compendium.

165

Now the observations described above are visual estimates, made and recorded as suggested (for example) in the AAVSO *Manual*. As understanding of the basic "model" for each kind of variable star improves, however, there arises need for greater and greater precision in the observational material. This increased precision can best be attained photoelectrically, by equipment and procedures such as those described by Code, Kron, and Bateson, earlier in this book, or (in somewhat less detail) in the *Handbook* of the Photoelectric Committee of the AAVSO. Broadly speaking, the effort to attain higher accuracy for the over-all light-curve of a variable centers on one or both of two main avenues of approach: (1) improvement in the magnitudes assigned the comparison stars used (whether the variable is compared with them visually or photoelectrically), and (2) direct photoelectric comparison of the variable with a set of comparison stars supposedly satisfactory for the purpose. The expanding program of the Variable Star Section of the New Zealand Astronomical Society, under the dynamic leadership of F. M. Bateson, shows clearly the lines of progress discussed here. "Magnificent observations of more than 200 variable stars are published systematically by that Section" (Kukarkin, Commission 27 *Report*, IAU, 1955). A new set of star charts for southern variables has been prepared and published by the Section. At this writing work is well under way for the establishment of an observatory in New Zealand devoted primarily to systematic photoelectric observation both of comparison star sequences and of variables themselves.

A great advantage of photoelectric technique is the relatively high degree of impersonalism which can be attained. By making measurements on stars of fields already carefully studied and "standardized," a given observer can select filters and reduction formulas whereby he can very closely approximate, for his own derived magnitudes of these stars and others, a "standard" magnitude-and-color system. His observations on a given star are then highly compatible with those made with other photoelectric equipment similarly standardized. It was because of the importance of this compatibility, so relatively easily arrived at in the photoelectric case, that Commission 42 (Eclipsing Binaries) of the International Astronomical Union, passed at its session at Moscow in 1958 the following "Resolution on Standards for Photoelectric Observations":

Commission 42 recommends that observers of eclipsing variables employing photoelectric equipment, use 2- or 3- wavelength filter-photocell equipment approximating in spectral response as closely as possible that of a well-established photometric system. The Commission recommends that each photoelectric observer publish his original observations, together with either the reductions to a standard system or information which will permit the observations to be reduced to a standard system.

We assume, then, an observer with standardized equipment. Dr. Paul Merrill remarked, in the article mentioned above, that his study shows that progress in the field of red stars has been great enough in recent years so that there now exists a clear need of photometric work if the reliability of the general conclusions is to be improved significantly in the foreseeable future. And in 1958 Mrs. Mayall wrote,

The selection of suitable comparison stars and determination of good magnitudes for them remains the greatest stumbling-block in the addition of new variable stars to an observing program. It is our great hope that more observatories with photoelectric equipment can be interested in obtaining good magnitude sequences on the visual scale for variables brighter than the eleventh magnitude at maximum.

It is therefore obvious that photoelectric measures on magnitudes and colors of comparison stars for intrinsic variables should be transmitted to the AAVSO for collation and publication.

In the parallel area of comparison stars for eclipsing variables, likewise, there is valuable work to be done, in both the northern and the southern hemisphere. In the eclipsing binary case, two further allied needs also press for satisfaction by photoelectric observation: (1) good colors are needed for many eclipsing variables, as a temporary substitute for the spectral types which accumulate so slowly; (2) precise times of minimum are needed for almost all eclipsing systems but especially for "close" systems and systems in rapid "evolution." The Center for Eclipsing Variables at the Cracow Observatory in Poland supplies charts and comparison star lists, prepared by Dr. K. Kordylewski, to northern observers seriously interested; Dr. Rosa Szafraniec of the same Center "has prepared charts for 146 southern eclipsing binaries, in the hope that amateur astronomers in the southern hemisphere will also join in this useful work." Hence photoelectric observations yielding magnitudes and/or colors of comparison stars for eclipsing variables, or yielding times of minimum for eclipsing

systems, should be transmitted to the Cracow Observatory for collation and publication. Since all published and much unpublished
material on eclipsing variables is listed in the Card Catalog maintained
at the Flower and Cook Observatory (University of Pennsylvania,
Philadelphia 4, Pennsylvania), the observations mentioned could be
sent to Dr. F. B. Wood instead of or in addition to transmitting them
to Cracow, but actual collating with the work of other observers is a
function of the Center at Cracow. An interesting note showing the
value of overlapping but independent observational programs appeared in the December 1960 issue of *Sky and Telescope*:

Donald K. Engelkemeir, Hinsdale, Illinois, reports photoelectric observations of the variable star Algol on October 1, 1960, finding that geocentric
minimum occurred at 5:11.6 UT, corresponding to Julian Day 2437208.7224
heliocentric. This is 33 minutes later than the *Sky and Telescope* prediction.
Dr. F. B. Wood writes that photoelectric observations at Flower and Cook
Observatory confirm this.

It thus appears that Algol's period has suffered a significant change
rather recently, a fact of considerable potential importance not simply
to observers but particularly to the theoreticians engaged in the effort
to unravel the many mysteries of the "Demon Star." In masterly
understatement the note goes on to say that "New determinations of
times of minima are highly desirable, whether visual or photoelectric. . . ."(!) On the one hand Engelkemeir in Illinois and Chou in
Pennsylvania could reasonably expect only a moderate amount of
telescope time, over the few months following this announcement,
suitable for determinations of times of minimum on this two-days- and-
five-hours star; on the other hand, it is impossible at one moment of
time to predict what changes will occur later. So observational series
yielding epochs reliable to 0.2 minutes or 0.3 minutes would be
welcomed, whether transmitted directly to Flower and Cook Observatory or through the Cracow Center.

Effective observation of flare stars such as UV Ceti, or the dMe-type
"flicker stars," and perhaps the peculiar A stars and the "recurrent
novae," almost demands the photocell, and even then it may not
always be possible to "go back to the comparison stars" as often as the
observer would like to (if at all!), things sometimes happen so fast
during an outburst. In these cases, where the phenomenon has been
recorded so infrequently, the fortunate observer of an outburst should

report on it directly to, for example, the *Publications of the Astronomical Society of the Pacific* as well as to his variable-star society, as Engelkemeir did for a flare of AD Leonis occurring on April 13, 1959.

It is clear from the cases cited above, that the observer of variable stars need not, and should not, operate entirely alone in planning an effective program. Cases exist where definite coordination of the observing effort itself can be expected to result in significantly more total understanding of a given object than the same amount of uncoordinated observing. Commissions 27 and 42 of the International Astronomical Union (Intrinsic Variables and Eclipsing Variables, respectively) have both sponsored intensive organized programs at selected times since their 1955 sessions, and it is to be presumed that further programs along the same lines will be undertaken. As an example, we may take the first such program, photoelectric observation of DD Lacertae, also known by its Flamsteed name of 12 Lacertae. We quote from the minutes of the joint session of the two Commisions held in one of the lecture rooms at Moscow University in August 1958:

Concerning the cooperative program on 12 Lacertae in the fall of 1956, Dr. de Jager reported that fifteen observatories (seven in Europe, seven in North America and one in Asia) undertook to obtain during a fourteen-day period a *continuous* [italics are ours] record of the star's brightness and color. This goal was not completely attained because the number of Asiatic observatories involved was insufficient [to offset the incidence of cloudiness], but valuable scientific results as well as important insights on conducting future cooperative programs, were obtained. For example, the 1956 observations showed that the amplitude in the secondary period was considerably less then than it had been in 1951–52. . . .

American amateurs can justifiably take some pride in the fact that John J. Ruiz, of Dannemora, New York, contributed 68 observations in two colors on three nights of the campaign.

As a demonstration of the potential value of a coordinated program for a selected eclipsing binary, K. K. Kwee of Leiden Observatory has stated that a total of 13,000 photoelectric observations on VW Cephei were reported made during the two intervals he selected for the concentrated attack on that star, and this total does not include the Soviet measures, which had not yet been reported. In these days of compatibility of measures and capability in communication, we are actually able to obtain continuous records of a star's variation covering several days—longitude, latitude, and consequent daylight notwith-standing! Obviously, here are situations in which some amateurs can make real and lasting contributions, for the nature of these programs is such that publication of good observations, and professional use of them, is practically guaranteed.

We can now go still one step farther, to the possibility of observation by one amateur or by one group of amateurs at one observatory, of the complete light curve of an eclipsing variable, preferably in two colors. This is probably the most demanding observational program one can set oneself in the field of variable stars, but in the series of measures on u Herculis by Ruiz we have proof that it can be carried through. In Chapter 6 above, Dr. Wood has set out basic philosophy and techniques for the production of a series adequate in number, in coverage, and in precision for determination of the principal characteristics of the two component stars of the system. The question remaining is then only of effective use of the observations made, and to this we give two answers.

First, it should be recognized both that some persons (professionals and amateurs alike) prefer to observe and to leave the utilization of observing results to others, and also that some persons like to carry through mathematical problems, perhaps even more than they like to observe. The amateur who (with necessarily limited time available for his pursuit of astronomy) prefers to concentrate on photoelectric observation, rather than to make solutions of his curves, should do just that. He should report his work to his local society and should send a complete list of the observations to Flower and Cook Observatory and to Cracow Observatory and (if he wishes) a summary report to the *Astronomical Journal* at Yale Observatory, the *Astronomische Nachrichten* in Germany, or to a suitable astronomical publication in his own country.

If, however, the observer would like to see grow out from his ob-servational material a picture of the geometry of the system and the surface characteristics of the stars, we invite him to explore with us in the succeeding pages, the system called u Herculis, as that system is defined by Ruiz's "blue" measures.

Table 7-1
u Herculis
Individual Observations in Blue by Ruiz

Norm. No.	Obs. No.	Phase θ	$\Delta m'$	Norm. No.	Obs. No.	Phase θ	$\Delta m'$
1	354	0.35	^{m}.719	8	298	22.47	^{m}.254
	151	0.88	.725		223	22.64	.259
	355	1.05	.725		173	22.82	.268
	310	1.58	.733		259	22.82	.273
	152	2.11	.724		224	24.05	.268
2	153	2.98	.693	9	299	24.40	.209
	356	4.39	.671		260	24.57	.262
	311	4.39	.688		174	24.92	.235
	312	5.09	.695		287	25.45	.242
	357	5.09	.670		225	25.80	.255
3	358	7.72	.656	10	261	26.15	.236
	292	8.25	.594		300	26.50	.187
	359	8.42	.621		175	26.85	.216
	313	8.60	.610		288	27.56	.226
	3	8.78	.623		226	27.56	.227
4	314	9.30	.601	11	46	27.73	.223
	293	10.00	.573		262	28.08	.216
	360	11.41	.540		301	28.61	.187
	315	11.41	.539		176	28.96	.193
	294	11.76	.505		47	29.14	.218
5	316	11.94	.524	12	289	29.49	.192
	168	12.81	.543		48	30.19	.189
	317	13.69	.475		263	30.54	.172
	4	14.04	.571		177	30.72	.195
	169	14.74	.468		270	31.24	.190
6	170	15.44	.433	13	49	31.77	.187
	295	15.97	.488		264	32.30	.179
	171	17.55	.385		178	32.65	.177
	296	18.25	.314		50	33.00	.171
	256	18.43	.352		271	33.00	.178
7	222	19.31	.379	14	265	34.05	.160
	172	19.66	.325		51	34.23	.144
	257	20.01	.337		42	34.93	.150
	297	20.54	.303		350	35.63	.137
	258	21.24	.293		52	35.63	.124

Table 7-1 (continued)
u Herculis
Individual Observations in Blue by Ruiz

Norm. No.	Obs. No.	Phase θ	$\Delta m'$	Norm. No.	Obs. No.	Phase θ	$\Delta m'$
15	290	35.63	^{m}.150	22	206	97.41	^{m}.043
	43	37.39	.140		285	97.94	.030
	291	37.74	.111		207	98.99	.038
	351	38.26	.122		286	102.33	.043
	44	38.79	.145		208	102.50	.049
16	352	38.96	.120	23	161	103.73	.045
	72	45.46	.105		209	103.91	.048
	73	47.22	.070		162	104.61	.039
	74	50.20	.086		210	105.49	.044
	75	51.95	.031		163	105.66	.023
17	76	53.71	.040	24	164	106.54	.059
	77	55.64	.059		165	107.42	.032
	78	57.22	.055		166	108.30	.052
	79	58.80	.073		167	109.35	.056
	217	59.50	.039		103	133.04	.056
18	218	61.26	.046	25	104	133.92	.049
	80	61.96	.055		105	137.61	.051
	219	62.48	.014		106	139.01	.081
	220	64.06	.032		15	140.07	.070
	221	67.75	.036		107	140.24	.064
19	119	80.74	.037	26	16	141.12	.062
	120	83.02	.035		17	143.75	.063
	121	84.25	.025		328	147.26	.090
	122	85.30	.022		329	147.96	.090
	123	86.53	.030		266	147.96	.085
20	200	87.23	.036	27	18	148.14	.056
	124	87.58	.025		19	148.49	.077
	201	88.99	.036		267	149.54	.086
	125	89.16	.035		330	149.90	.072
	202	90.74	.017		20	149.90	.084
21	203	92.15	.021	28	331	150.60	.087
	204	93.90	.036		268	151.30	.099
	283	94.96	.038		21	152.35	.111
	284	95.66	.039		332	152.53	.122
	205	95.66	.035		333	153.23	.123

Table 7-1 (continued)
u Herculis
Individual Observations in Blue by Ruiz

Norm. No.	Obs. No.	Phase θ	$\Delta m'$	Norm. No.	Obs. No.	Phase θ	$\Delta m'$
		°				°	
29	155	154.11	^{m}.104	36	326	180.61	^{m}.259
	156	154.98	.129		362	180.61	.280
	269	154.98	.127		327	181.49	.265
	22	155.16	.099		274	182.19	.281
	334	155.69	.121		363	182.72	.284
30	157	156.04	.130	37	179	185.18	.263
	23	156.04	.112		180	186.76	.262
	158	156.92	.126		53	186.76	.270
	90	157.62	.133		275	187.81	.254
	159	157.97	.162		54	188.16	.248
31	335	158.50	.125	38	84	188.51	.243
	160	158.85	.170		181	188.69	.230
	91	158.85	.157		55	189.56	.238
	336	159.02	.149		56	191.14	.232
	92	160.25	.151		85	191.32	.224
32	337	161.66	.150	39	182	191.67	.224
	93	161.66	.161		183	192.20	.216
	338	162.18	.140		57	192.55	.221
	94	162.88	.144		86	192.90	.228
	95	164.81	.194		276	193.78	.240
33	96	166.04	.192	40	184	194.13	.196
	97	167.27	.181		87	194.65	.191
	98	168.68	.241		185	195.88	.184
	318	169.55	.198		88	196.58	.198
	99	169.90	.246		186	197.46	.160
34	319	170.08	.222	41	89	198.34	.158
	320	172.19	.225		187	199.04	.150
	321	172.71	.231		188	200.97	.138
	322	175.00	.240		189	202.73	.113
	323	175.70	.244		190	204.31	.130
35	272	177.10	.261	42	191	205.71	.136
	324	177.80	.270		81	207.29	.065
	325	178.33	.257		82	210.45	.066
	273	179.38	.283		45	211.33	.096
	361	179.91	.288		83	212.03	.066

Table 7-1 (continued)
u Herculis
Individual Observations in Blue by Ruiz

Norm. No.	Obs. No.	Phase θ	$\Delta m'$	Norm. No.	Obs. No.	Phase θ	$\Delta m'$
43	138	218.52	^{m}.077	51	246	255.03	^{m}.017
	139	219.93	.063		212	256.26	.034
	140	220.81	.071		247	256.96	.037
	141	221.68	.072		348	257.49	.020
	142	223.61	.060		126	257.84	.030
44	143	224.49	.050	52	349	258.19	.020
	251	225.19	.058		248	258.72	.034
	144	225.55	.065		127	259.07	.026
	145	226.42	.060		213	259.95	.040
	252	226.95	.050		249	260.30	.032
45	132	227.30	.068	53	128	260.30	.034
	40	227.65	.053		214	261.70	.036
	146	227.83	.065		215	264.86	.028
	133	228.35	.037		250	265.04	.041
	253	228.53	.049		109	266.62	.041
46	134	229.41	.042	54	216	266.79	.025
	254	230.11	.042		110	267.85	.033
	135	230.46	.031		111	269.07	.021
	255	231.51	.039		112	270.30	.027
	136	231.51	.057		241	271.01	.032
47	41	231.86	.019	55	113	271.71	.040
	137	232.57	.050		242	272.41	.026
	69	235.55	.044		114	272.94	.023
	34	236.60	.046		243	273.64	.039
	70	237.31	.035		31	273.99	.025
48	343	237.66	.026	56	115	275.04	.050
	35	237.83	.045		116	276.27	.042
	36	239.06	.027		32	277.15	.039
	129	239.94	.040		192	277.68	.030
	344	240.11	.030		118	278.55	.048
49	345	240.99	.034	57	193	279.08	.059
	130	241.17	.047		33	279.96	.052
	131	242.04	.019		194	280.48	.048
	346	243.62	.035		244	281.36	.056
	347	244.33	.032		195	281.89	.034
50	37	245.91	.020	58	196	283.64	.044
	38	248.71	.032		30	285.05	.029
	39	249.94	.018		197	286.45	.040
	245	254.16	.039		198	288.21	.053
	211	254.51	.042		199	289.79	.056

Table 7-1 (continued)
u Herculis
Individual Observations in Blue by Ruiz

Norm. No.	Obs. No.	Phase θ	$\Delta m'$	Norm. No.	Obs. No.	Phase θ	$\Delta m'$
59	108	294.53	^{m}.048	67	279	334.90	^{m}.229
	339	295.58	.055		237	334.90	.296
	340	296.28	.062		61	335.95	.293
	341	298.74	.063		1	336.12	.301
	342	299.44	.065		62	337.53	.305
60	66	307.16	.102	68	2	337.70	.301
	67	308.57	.081		280	337.70	.278
	68	309.80	.093		63	338.93	.310
	24	309.80	.109		281	339.99	.347
	25	312.08	.127		64	340.16	.319
61	238	312.96	.093	69	65	341.39	.364
	239	314.36	.093		10	341.74	.384
	26	315.59	.133		11	343.50	.452
	240	315.94	.122		282	343.85	.435
	227	318.40	.127		13	346.48	.510
62	27	318.57	.136	70	14	348.24	.529
	5	319.27	.107		364	348.24	.510
	228	320.50	.112		365	348.94	.538
	102	320.68	.115		302	350.34	.654
	6	321.38	.161				
				71	366	351.75	.618
63	229	322.08	.157		303	352.10	.671
	230	323.66	.155		367	352.62	.672
	28	325.77	.159		304	354.20	.732
	231	326.30	.172				
				72	305	355.61	.732
64	232	327.70	.185		147	356.31	.727
	29	328.23	.154		306	356.48	.721
	233	329.10	.191		307	357.01	.737
	234	330.68	.194		148	357.36	.718
	58	331.03	.198				
				73	353	357.89	.717
65	100	331.39	.225		149	358.42	.743
	8	331.56	.203		308	358.94	.739
	277	331.74	.237		309	359.47	.739
	235	331.91	.241		150	359.64	.717
	59	332.79	.250				
66	101	332.79	.231				
	278	332.96	.249				
	236	333.67	.245				
	60	334.37	.261				
	9	334.72	.219				

PART II

As its Bayer name implies, u Herculis is a rather faint naked eye star. It stands (right ascension 17^h 16^m, declination 33.°1, 1960) about three degrees east of the southern part of the famous Keystone, but its very blue color (the spectral classes of its components are B3 and B7) and its apparent magnitude (4.5 at maximum, 5.2 at primary minimum) combine to make it a difficult object for most people except on a clear moonless night. It has been known as an eclipsing binary of the Beta Lyrae type since Wendell observed it visually with his polarizing photometer at Harvard near the turn of the century.

Studies of the light curves and radial velocity curves published up to 1937 (Keutmann and Miczaika, *Astronomische Nachrichten*, **261**: 205, 1937 and Martin, *Bulletin of the Astronomical Institutes of the Netherlands*, **8**: 265, 1938) indicate that the period has been constant and that the orbit is sensibly circular; both these conclusions are borne out by the more recent spectrographic curve by Smith (*Astrophysical Journal*, **102**: 500, 1945) and the photoelectric series by John J. Ruiz (*Publications of the Astronomical Society of the Pacific*, **69**: 261, 1957). This latter series comprises 362 observations in the blue (effective wavelength 4,050Å) and an equal number in the yellow (5,300Å) and is therefore the most extensive homogeneous photometric material presently available on u Herculis. We treat here only the blue curve, though much additional information should result from intercomparison with results from the yellow one. Ruiz has the observational material—magnitude-difference relative to 59 Herculis as standard versus phase in days—all arranged in order of phase on Calder's elements (primary minimum J. D. 2427640.654 $+$ $2\overset{d}{.}051027E$) just like that used herein. Perhaps some readers will decide to practice on the yellow! In the meantime, let us get to work on the blue.

176

We convert Ruiz' phases in days to phases in degrees counted from his zero, by

$$\theta° = \frac{360}{2.051027} = 175.5218 \times \text{(phase in days)}$$

and his magnitude-difference $\Delta m = 59 - u$ to a set $\Delta m' = 1.050 - \Delta m$. This phase conversion places the observations in orbital longitude counted from the conjunction at which the greater light-loss occurs, while the magnitude conversion (with its zero chosen just brighter than the brightest listed observation) yields magnitude differences increasing with decreasing brightness of the variable and thereby in most convenient form for converting later to relative intensity. Separating the individual observations into groups of five consecutive (except for three cases of four each), we have the four columns of Table 7-1. Taking straight averages in θ and then in $\Delta m'$, within the groups set off in Table 7-1, gives us the first three columns of Table 7-2, then conversion of $\Delta m'$ to relative intensity $\mathfrak{I}$ by use of Appendix Table II easily yields column 4, while a "trig table," preferably in decimals of a degree, yields columns 5 and 6. We also prepare, in similar fashion, the first six columns of Table 7-3; this table is not actually necessary, but will give a useful check at one point of our work later. We now have the basic tables for our solution, so a plot of the normals, $\Delta m'$ against θ, with about the proportions shown in Figure 7-1 and with a horizontal scale of 20° per inch or per centimeter (according to taste), completes the preparatory phase of our study.

Onto the observational plot just mentioned we shall later draw the "computed curve" resulting from the two-stage analysis: (1) from the between-eclipse portions of the observational data (the "tops") we shall determine the degree to which tidal forces and centrifugal effects have distorted the two stars out of spherical, and the degree to which interradiation has brightened the sides of the stars that face each other; (2) from the within-eclipse portions of the observational data (the "eclipses"), altered to compensate for the shape and reflection effects, we shall determine the sizes of the two stars relative to each other and to the distance between their centers, the contribution of each to the total light emitted, the percentage of the light of each obscured at maximum eclipse, and the angle at which we view the revolving system. Quite an agenda! Each of the two stages yields,

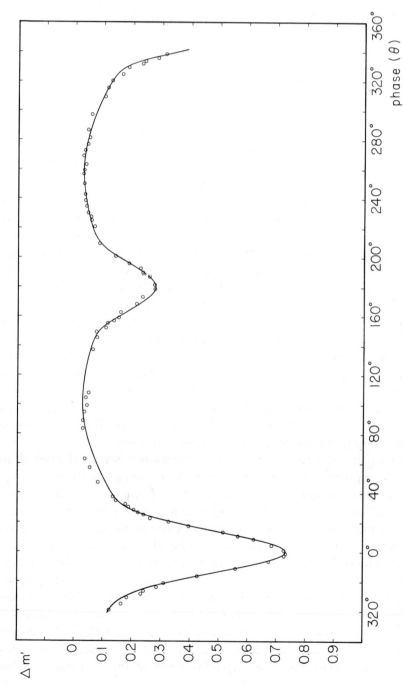

Figure 7-1. u Herculis: Normals and adopted curve.

then, a significant portion of the total system-description; the over-all reasonableness of that description will be shown by the synthesized computed curve, but the detailed, step-by-step judgments will be made on other charts.

(1) *Study of the tops*

We now plot the normals for the tops, $\mathfrak{I}$ against θ, with $10°$ to an inch for θ and a scale for $\mathfrak{I}$ giving good but not excessive bowing to the curve, in this case 0.05 of $\mathfrak{I}$ to an inch. It is obvious from the $\Delta m'(\Theta)$ plot (which we use throughout as a general guide) that we cannot say at this moment just where the eclipses end and the tops begin, so we include one or two extra points at each end of each top. It is also obvious that the kind of system characteristics we are seeking all display themselves in symmetrical effects, so the second top would be (ideally) simply the reverse of the first one. We therefore plot the second top "reflected" onto the first (just by running its scale backward along that for the first), using, say, blue ink for the "direct" and red ink for the "reflected" points so that significant differences will show up but not obtrude. Figure 7-2 thus carries normals 10 through 30 and 41 through 67.

We now draw a reasonable *freehand* curve *among* the points. Our aim is to achieve as soon as possible satisfactory representation by a *mathematical* curve of the form $A_0 + A_1 \cos \theta + A_2 \cos 2\theta$, so snake-like wiggles for the sake of slavishly passing this freehand curve *through* every normal point make no sense. To adjust this freehand curve to the run of the normals it is well to read residuals and take averages in, say, $20°$ sections, keeping direct and reflected separate; then a little work with eraser and pencil should bring out a sensible compromise in a couple of tries. The final freehand curve obtained in this manner is drawn among the normals in Figure 7-2. (Note also the discrepancy between branches showing up in the $50°$, $60°$ neighborhood.)

We now read intensities at every $5°$ from this freehand curve; those from the $30°$-to-$90°$ section inclusive we call "a" (by convention only), those from the $90°$-to-$150°$ section inclusive we call "b". Tabulating a against θ, b against $180° - \theta$, then $(a + b)/2$ and $(a - b)/2$, $\cos \theta$ and $\cos 2\theta$, we have Table 7-4, which constitutes our data for deriving the desired function $I = A_0 + A_1 \cos \theta + A_2 \cos 2\theta$.

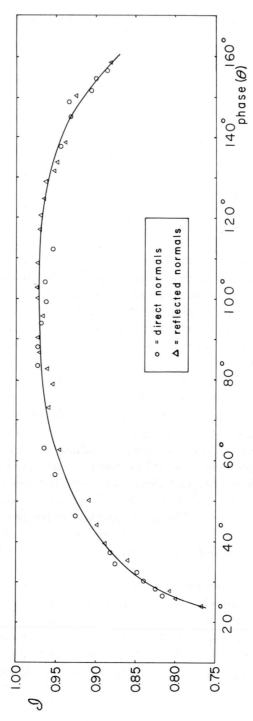

Figure 7-2. u Herculis: Normals and free-hand curve for tops.

It is helpful to make a quick first approximation now: A_0 will usually turn out nearly equal to the value of $(a + b)/2$ for $\theta = 45°$; A_1 will be 1.41 times $(a - b)/2$ for $\theta = 45°$; A_2 will be $(a + b)/2$ for $45°$ *minus* $(a + b)/2$ for $90°$. In the present case we can therefore expect the function to be, roughly, $I_1 = 0.9305 - 0.0304 \cos \theta - 0.0405 \cos 2\theta$, where the subscript denotes our first trial I. This curve $I_1 (\theta)$ is plotted on tracing paper, but shown here in Figure 7-3; it is clear that it is a fair fit *to the normal points*, but can probably be improved upon.

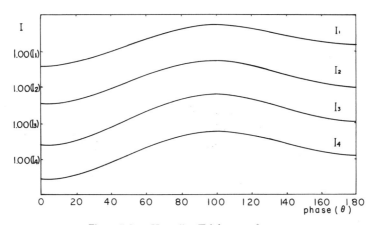

Figure 7-3. u Herculis: Trial curves for tops.

For a better over-all agreement we now make two plots: $(a - b)/2$ against $\cos \theta$, and $(a + b)/2$ against $\cos 2\theta$, as shown in Figure 7-4. Note that for ease in making three-way comparisons, the vertical scales of both should increase upward, 0.05 per inch, while the horizontal scales should be 0.10 of $\cos \theta$ per inch and 0.20 of $\cos 2\theta$ per inch respectively; the 90° points should be to the right of the 30° ones on both charts. It will be helpful now, and also later, if we provide ourselves with a "trial line," a straight line about 10 inches long scribed and inked on a rectangle of 0.015-inch transparent plastic; this is not necessary, of course, but serves the purpose of a trial line much better than a ruler edge or a thread.

The plot of $(a - b)/2$ against $\cos \theta$ is to give us the coefficient A_1. If the observations were perfect, the free-hand curve a perfect fit to

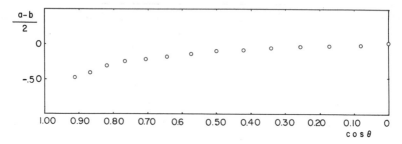

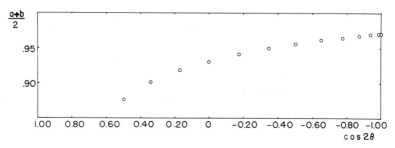

Figure 7-4. u Herculis: Plots of Data from Table 7-4.
Top, for Determination of A_1
Bottom, for Determination of A_0 and A_2

them, *and the system model a perfect representation of nature*, then all the points from $\theta = 90°$ leftward to the (presently unknown) shoulder of eclipse would lie on a straight line of slope A_1 passing through (0,0), i.e., through the 90° point. Our trial line, laid on the plot so as to pass through (0,0) shows at once that the points down to, say, 40° are nearly collinear but not quite. We note, next, that the coefficient -0.0304 we used in I_1, is simply the slope of the line through the 90° and the 45° points, and also that the easiest way to get a slope A_1 is simply to read the vertical coordinate of the trial line at the $\cos \theta = 1.00$ (left) end of the chart. We now see also that the departure of the 30° point from the general straight run indicates that it (at least) is just inside the eclipse region; we therefore now disregard it and set the trial line so as to represent a reasonable mean of the rest while still passing through (0,0). We now get — 0.025 as A_1 for our second approximation.

We now consider the plot of $(a + b)/2$ against $\cos 2\theta$, from which we shall obtain A_0 and A_2. The reasoning is very similar to the above, differing in detail and in the important fact that there is no fixed point through which we must pass the trial line. In any case, the vertical coordinate of its intersection with $\cos 2\theta = 0$ will be A_0, and A_2 will be the result of substracting its intercept on $\cos 2\theta = -1.00$ (extreme right) from the intercept on $\cos 2\theta = 0$. Again we see that the 30° point deviates appreciably and the 35° point slightly from any reasonable straight-line approximation to the other points. We take 0.925 as A_0 and $0.925 - 0.972 = -0.047$ as A_2 for our second approximation.

We now plot $I_2 = 0.925 - 0.025 \cos \theta - 0.047 \cos 2\theta$ on tracing paper (Figure 7-3) just as we plotted I_1, and compare *both* with the plot of the tops. A little mental juggling of the curves shows at once that we need "a little more A_1 and perhaps a little more A_2," so we try $I_3 = 0.925 - 0.035 \cos \theta - 0.052 \cos 2\theta$, (Figure 7-3) but this curve bows too much. We revert to $I_4 = 0.925 - 0.035 \cos \theta - 0.047 \cos 2\theta$, which, upon plotting as in Figure 7-3, seems quite satisfactory as a representation of the normal points. We note also that in the process it has become pretty clear that the discrepancy we noted at the beginning, between the run of the points in the 50°, 60° neighborhood, is to be ascribed to an excess of brightness just after primary eclipse is over rather than to a deficiency just before primary eclipse begins.

We now look more closely at the run of the observational points, on the plot of the tops, relative to the adopted theoretical curve I_4, in the vicinity of the eclipse shoulders, and at the same time at the run of corresponding points on the $\cos \theta$ and $\cos 2\theta$ charts relative to the adopted straight lines. Certainly the 30° point is well inside the eclipse, the 40° point safely outside; a few sketchings with a pencil leads us to feel that the eclipse shoulder is at $\theta = 35°$ or 36°; we adopt 35° for the present, subject to later change if needed. (We denote this by θ_e, meaning "θ at external tangency.") We note further that the shape of the original light curve, $\Delta m'$ against θ, makes it almost certain that the eclipses are partial at deepest phase.

Assuming the eclipses as partial we can set out three constants defining the interradiation effects:

$$C_0 = 0.090 \sin^2 \theta_e = +0.0263$$
$$C_1 = -A_1 = +0.0350$$
$$C_2 = 0.030 \sin^2 \theta_e = +0.00855$$

yielding the form

$$\mathfrak{I}' = \mathfrak{I} + 0.0263 + 0.0350 \cos \theta + 0.00855 \cos 2\theta$$

by which to adjust the observations $\mathfrak{I}$ to new values $\mathfrak{I}'$ such that the "backs" of the two components of the system will be of the same brightness as the hemispheres facing each other, instead of fainter. (Had the eclipses been total-annular, we would have used

$$C_0 = 0.072 \sin^2\theta_e$$
$$C_1 = -A_1$$
$$C_2 = 0.024 \sin^2\theta_e$$

instead of the forms given above.)

Having (in imagination if not in actuality) corrected the normals in the tops for the interradiation effect by this *additive* process, we turn to the adjustment of the new intensities $\mathfrak{I}'$ to take account of the tidal distortions of the components. This is accomplished by *dividing* each $\mathfrak{I}'$ by $[(A_0 + C_0) + (A_2 + C_2)\cos 2\theta]$, in this case by computing

$$\mathfrak{I}'' = \frac{\mathfrak{I}'}{0.9513 - 0.03845 \cos 2\theta}$$

or

$$\mathfrak{I}'' = \frac{\mathfrak{I} + 0.0263 + 0.0350 \cos \theta + 0.00855 \cos 2\theta}{0.9513 - 0.03845 \cos 2\theta}$$

for the normals in the tops. Whether the conversion of $\mathfrak{I}$ to $\mathfrak{I}''$ is made in one or several steps, is of course only a question of convenience or taste; we have not listed the values of $\mathfrak{I}'$ in Table 7-2, but have gone directly to $\mathfrak{I}''$.

"The proof of the pudding is in the eating," so we now check our numerical work and the adequacy of our set of constants by plotting $\mathfrak{I}''$ against θ to the same scales as before (Figure 7-5), and by calculating the mean $\mathfrak{I}''$ for normals 14 through 27 and 42 through 62. Since this mean is 1.0007 and the plot looks satisfactory, discounting the 50°, 60° deviation already recognized, we accept the derived constants as reasonable, and proceed next to adjust the normals within the eclipses to take account of the interradiation and tidal effects they define.

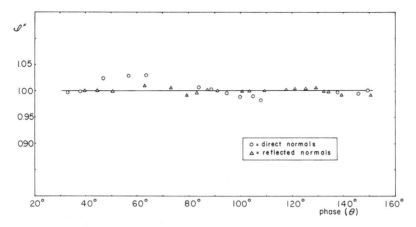

Figure 7-5. u Herculis: Normals in Tops Corrected for Ellipticity
and Reflection.

(2) *Study of the Eclipses*

First we adjust the observed intensities inside eclipse by converting each $\mathfrak{I}$ to $\mathfrak{I}''$, thus completing column 7 of Tables 7-2 and 7-3. Next by the formula $z = \dfrac{1.54(C_2 - A_2)}{A_0 - C_0 - A_2 + C_2}$ we find $z = 0.09$; using this in Table 7-5 we convert each θ inside eclipse and one or two extra at each shoulder, to $\sin \Theta$ (z, θ), obtaining column 8 of Tables 7-2 and 7-3. It is the pairs $(\sin \Theta, \mathfrak{I}'')$, not $(\theta, \mathfrak{I})$, which form our data for study of the eclipses themselves. We shall be more specific on the matter of interpretation when we come to gathering up all the derived information, at the end of our study; for now we note merely that by this process we have in essence replaced the two revolving elliptical components suffering reflection effects with two spherical components free of such effects.

With the relative orbit assumed circular, both eclipses are to be assumed symmetrical, so we now plot $\mathfrak{I}''$ against $\sin \Theta$ for primary eclipse, with the points of the descending branch "reflected" over onto the ascending, and distinguished from them by use of red ink. The scales should be very "open" and the average slope should be 45° or less; the scales of the working plot from which Figure 7-6 was made were: for $\sin \Theta$, $0.05 = 1$ inch, for $\mathfrak{I}''$, $0.10 = 1$ inch. Secondary is of course to be plotted to the same scales, and indeed may well be placed just a few spaces higher on the same sheet to facilitate comparisons.

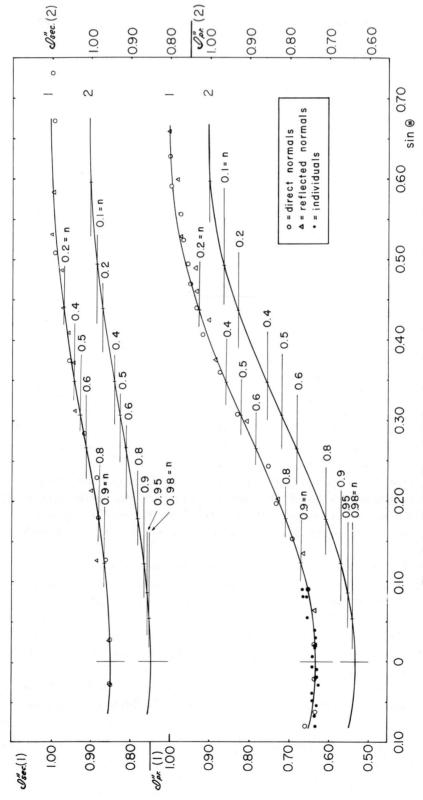

Figure 7-6. u Herculis J'' vs. sin Θ for eclipses. Secondary curves are above, primary below. (1) Data, Free-Hand Curves and Scales for Them; (2) Adopted Curves and Scales for Them.

The points of Table 7-3 should be added to the plot of primary; oftentimes it is useful to add individual points also around the 0 of secondary, but in this case it did not seem worthwhile.

The theoretical top, 1.000, has already been established. Consideration of the mean values for points close to $\sin \Theta = 0$, and a few tries with freehand curves there, lead at once to the preliminary values for minimum light $l_0^{pr} = 0.635$ and $l_0^{sec} = 0.850$. We therefore now draw freehand curves from these levels upward among the normal points, presumably reaching unit level at *about* $\sin \Theta = 0.592$ ($\theta = 35°$) but of course not "forcing" the curves; we then make such minor adjustments in these freehand curves as group means of the residuals points-minus-curve seem to indicate.

Denoting the relative light-loss $\dfrac{(1 - l)}{(1 - l_0)}$ at any point by the symbol "n," we draw level-lines at $n = 0.2, 0.4, 0.5, 0.6, 0.8,$ and 0.9 across the curves and read off the corresponding values of $\sin \Theta$ (n) as follows.

Secondary Eclipse, $1 - l_0^{sec} = 0.150$

n	$1 - l^{sec}$	$\sin \Theta$ (n)
0.2	.030	.437
0.4	.060	.345
0.5	.075	.301
0.6	.090	.259
0.8	.120	.175
0.9	.135	.115

Primary Eclipse, $1 - l_0^{pr} = 0.365$

n	$1 - l^{pr}$	$\sin \Theta$ (n)
0.2	.073	.440
0.4	.146	.345
0.5	.182	.306
0.6	.219	.264
0.8	.292	.177
0.9	.328	.120

Usually it is well to read also at $n = 0.1, 0.3,$ and 0.7, and "difference" the nine values in order, as a check on reasonableness, but in the present example the readings were checked by another person instead.

For	depth-line cuts	at scale reading
	EI	$(1 - l_o^{tr}) + (1 - l_o^{oc})$
partial eclipses	BS	$\dfrac{1 - l_o^{tr}}{l_o^{oc}} + \dfrac{1}{50}\dfrac{1 - l_o^{oc}}{l_o^{oc}}$
	TI	$\dfrac{1 - l^{tr}}{l_o^{oc}}$
total-annular eclipses	both TI and BS	$\dfrac{1 - l^{tr}}{l_o^{oc}}$

Possible solution	is shown by intersection of
P_1	line and χ^{pr} contour
P_2	line and χ^{sec} contour
P_3	χ^{pr} and χ^{sec} contours

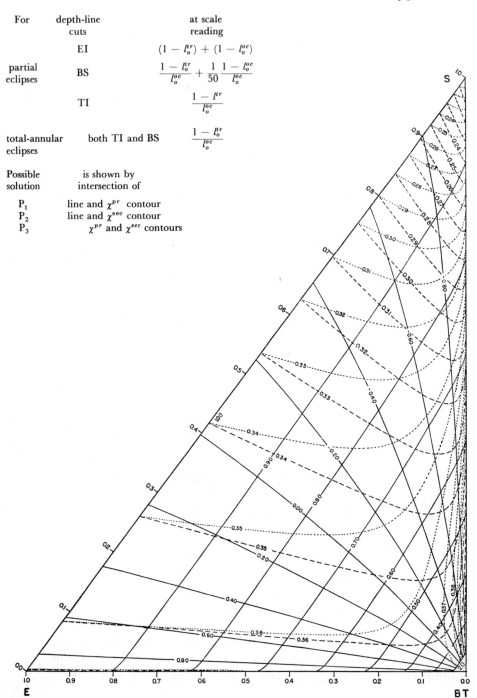

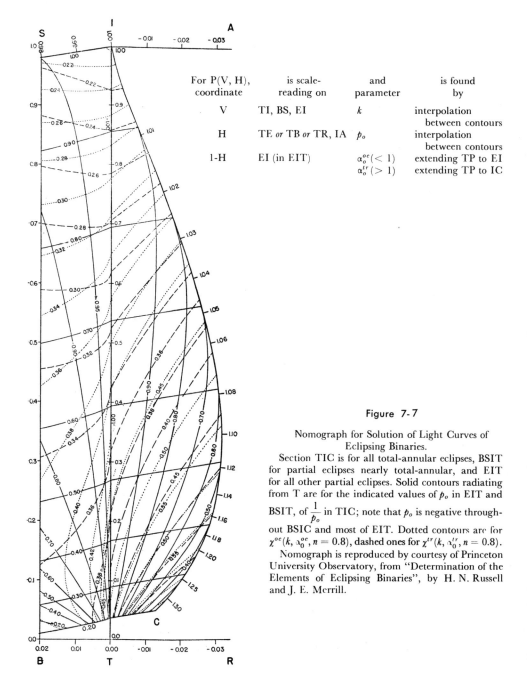

For P(V, H),

coordinate	is scale-reading on	and parameter	is found by
V	TI, BS, EI	k	interpolation between contours
H	TE *or* TB *or* TR, IA	p_o	interpolation between contours
1-H	EI (in EIT)	$\alpha_o^{oc}(<1)$	extending TP to EI
		$\alpha_o^{tr}(>1)$	extending TP to IC

Figure 7-7

Nomograph for Solution of Light Curves of Eclipsing Binaries.

Section TIC is for all total-annular eclipses, BSIT for partial eclipses nearly total-annular, and EIT for all other partial eclipses. Solid contours radiating from T are for the indicated values of p_o in EIT and BSIT, of $\frac{1}{p_o}$ in TIC; note that p_o is negative throughout BSIC and most of EIT. Dotted contours are for $\chi^{oc}(k, \alpha_0^{oc}, n = 0.8)$, dashed ones for $\chi^{tr}(k, \alpha_0^{tr}, n = 0.8)$.

Nomograph is reproduced by courtesy of Princeton University Observatory, from "Determination of the Elements of Eclipsing Binaries", by H. N. Russell and J. E. Merrill.

Defining a new quantity χ by $\chi(0.8) = \dfrac{\sin^2\Theta(0.8)}{\sin^2\Theta(0.5)}$, we compute $\chi_1^{pr}(0.8) = 0.336$ and also $\chi_1^{sec}(0.8) = 0.340$, where the subscript 1 denotes the first try. We note that because of the shallowness of secondary eclipse in this particular case $\chi^{sec}(0.8)$ is probably less reliable than $\chi^{pr}(0.8)$, although the depth $(1 - l_0^{sec})$ itself is presumably as well determined as $(1 - l_0^{pr})$. *To the extent* that the values of $\sin\Theta(n)$ in secondary can be trusted, however, we are now in a position to make two important statements about the system:

(1) The near equality of the corresponding values of $\sin\Theta(n)$ implies that the two components of the system are nearly of the same size.

(2) Since $\chi^{sec}(0.8)$ is greater than $\chi^{pr}(0.8)$, the (slightly) larger component is in front during secondary eclipse. We express this by saying that primary eclipse is a "transit," secondary an "occultation."

The nomograph of Figure 7-7 is the basis for our "solution." Essentially it is a chart of the theoretical relationships between the shapes of eclipse-curves on the one hand and the relative sizes and maximum percentages of obscuration of the components on the other. Ideally, a "solution" is represented by the intersection of the appropriate $\chi^{oc}(0.8)$ contour, $\chi^{tr}(0.8)$ contour, and a "depth line" laid on according to the instructions given; practically, it seldom happens that the first-try data yield such a clean-cut situation. In the present case, for example, we have initially four positions of the depth line to look at, and for no one of them do the two contours and the line meet at a common point. Chins up! A first approximation gives us the means to make a much firmer second approximation.

We have four positions of the depth line to look at because strictly we do not yet *know* whether the eclipses are partial or total-annular at maximum and do not yet *know* whether primary is transit or occultation. Since, however, we have some reason to *believe* that the eclipses are partial, with primary a transit, we shall pretty much leave the two cases of primary as occultation to the reader as an exercise in negation.

For primary as transit partial the depth line runs from 0.515 on *EI* downward to the right across the triangle to 0.430 on *IT*, while for primary as annular it runs from $IT = 0.430$ horizontally to the right across the bulgy region *TIC*. It is obvious at once that primary as annular is very unlikely: the contour $\chi^{oc}(0.8) = 0.340$ (unreliable though it may be) is nowhere near the depth line in *TIC*; the partial-eclipse line, however, suggests two possibilities, which we proceed to investigate: (1) if the values of sin $\Theta(0.8)$ from freehand curves have *slightly* overestimated χ^{tr} and χ^{oc}, a solution may exist near *EI*; (2) if we practically disregard the preliminary value of $\chi^{oc}(0.8)$, a solution might turn out to exist near *IT*.

To study these two possibilities we read off rough values of three system parameters:

$$k = \frac{r_s}{r_g} = \frac{\text{radius of smaller star}}{\text{radius of greater star}}$$

$$\alpha_0^{oc} = \frac{1 - l_0^{oc}}{L_s} = \frac{\text{maximum light loss in } oc \text{ eclipse}}{\text{total light of smaller star}}$$

$$\alpha_0^{tr} = \frac{1 - l_0^{tr}}{\tau L_g} = \frac{\text{maximum light loss in } tr \text{ eclipse}}{\text{light of greater star lost at internal tangency}}$$

and by use of Tables 7-6 *oc* and 7-6 *tr* "improve" on the values of sin $\Theta(0.8)$ and thereby the χ's. (The depths and therefore the depth line are known to be much more firmly established already.)

(1) We take the 0.515 point on *EI*, for which $k = 1.00$, $\alpha_0^{oc} = 0.515$, α_0^{tr} ($= \alpha_0^{oc}$ for equal stars) $= 0.515$; by Table 7-6 we alter the values of sin $\Theta(n)$ previously read from the freehand curves to obtain fictitious values of sin $\Theta(0.8)$.

Secondary Eclipse

n	sin $\Theta(n)$ (freehand)	$\dfrac{\text{sin } \Theta(0.8)}{\text{sin } \Theta(n)}$	fictitious sin $\Theta(0.8)$
0.2	.437	.402	.176
0.4	.345	.507	.175
0.5	.301	———	———
0.6	.259	.665	.172
0.8	.175	1.000	.175
0.9	.115	1.454	.167
mean			.173

Since the fictitious values are in good agreement with the original sin $\Theta(0.8)$, we seem to be on firm ground and therefore regard the mean as an improved value for sin $\Theta(0.8)$, and therefore $\left(\dfrac{.173}{.301}\right)^2 = .331$ as our second approximation to $\chi^{oc}(0.8)$.

Primary Eclipse

n	$\sin \Theta (n)$ (freehand)	$\dfrac{\sin \Theta (0.8)}{\sin \Theta (n)}$	fictitious $\sin \Theta (0.8)$
0.2	.440	.402	.177
0.4	.345	.507	.175
0.5	.306	——	——
0.6	.264	.665	.176
0.8	.177	1.000	.177
0.9	.120	1.454	.174
mean			.176

Again the agreement is excellent. We take $\chi^{tr}(0.8) = \left(\dfrac{.176}{.306}\right)^2 = .331$ as our second approximation and we note also that both χ's did decrease just a little.

(2) We take the point on IT where $k = .625$. Since IT is the internal-tangency line, $\alpha_0^{oc} = 1.00$ and $\alpha_0^{tr} = 1.00$.

Secondary Eclipse

n	$\sin \Theta (n)$ (freehand)	$\dfrac{\sin \Theta (0.8)}{\sin \Theta (n)}$	fictitious $\sin \Theta (0.8)$
0.2	.437	.458	.200
0.4	.345	.564	.195
0.5	.301	——	——
0.6	.259	.714	.185
0.8	.175	1.000	.175
0.9	.115	1.337	.154

This is quite incredible: either the freehand curve in secondary is wholly untrustworthy, or the assumption of near-internal-tangency eclipse is untenable.

Primary Eclipse

n	$\sin \Theta (n)$ (freehand)	$\dfrac{\sin \Theta (0.8)}{\sin \Theta (n)}$	fictitious $\sin \Theta (0.8)$
0.2	.440	.403	.177
0.4	.345	.511	.176
0.5	.306	——	——
0.6	.264	.673	.178
0.8	.177	1.000	.177
0.9	.120	1.417	.170
mean			.176

The agreement is excellent! And the value of $\chi^{tr}(0.8)$ implied is $\left(\dfrac{.176}{.306}\right)^2 = .331$! We therefore have been pushed by the numbers themselves to the conclusion that $\chi^{tr}(0.8) = 0.331$, that $\chi^{oc}(0.8)$ is probably about 0.331 and that the assumption of a solution near IT is negated by the shape of secondary. We therefore return now to the nomograph with our improved χ's and our same depth line. The situation is now perfectly clear: a solution does exist close to but not quite on EI. Since the value $\chi^{tr}(0.8) = .331$ is probably *slightly* firmer than $\chi^{oc}(0.8) = .331$, and since we *must* stay on the depth-line (or alter the depths, which are by their nature firmer than either χ), we adopt as second approximation the point where the depth line crosses the (imagined) contour $\chi^{tr}(0.8) = .331$.

There are two convenient ways of deriving some of the constants which this point (call it P) represents, and it is well to use both ways as a check, even though they are not completely independent: essentially, one method consists in interpolating between nomograph contours, the other in use of the vertical and horizontal coordinates of P in appropriate formulas and tables.

The boundary EI is also the contour $k = 1.00$, so P is at $k = .98$, very nearly; in a total-annular case P (in TIC) would be found in the same way. The line TP cuts EI at 0.53, so $\alpha_0^{oc} = .53$; in TIC, TP would cut IC at α_0^{tr}. The line through P parallel to EI cuts both ET and IT at .96,

so $q_0\left(=\dfrac{\alpha_0^{tr}\tau}{\alpha_0^{oc}}\right) = .96$; in TIC, $q_0 = \dfrac{1 - l_0^{tr}}{l_0^{oc}}$ itself. From the p_0 contours,

$p_0 = -.21$; in TIC the contours are for $1/p_0$. By Table 7-7 , $\tau = .975$

and therefore $\alpha_0^{tr} = \dfrac{\alpha_0^{oc}q_0}{\tau} = .52$; in TIC, the line through P parallel to the k contours cuts IT at τ.

Let V and H be the vertical and horizontal coordinates of P, respectively. Then V can be read directly on EI, IT, or SB, in all cases; for P in EIT, H can be read directly on ET or as $(1 - $ the EI reading) while for P in TIC, H is read on TR or IA and is always negative. Exercising some care in both setting and reading we find for our case $V = .509$, $H = .448$, probably good to a couple of units of the third decimal, and checking satisfactorily in the line equation $V\,l_0^{oc} = H(1 - l_0^{oc}) + (1 - l_0^{tr})$. Then $q_0 = V + H = .957$ and $\alpha_0^{oc} = \dfrac{V}{V + H} = .532$. By

Table 7-8, $k = .978$ and $p_0 = -.209$, then by Table 7-7, $\tau = .972$ and therefore $\alpha_0^{tr} = \dfrac{V}{\tau} = .524$. For P in TIC, $\alpha_0^{oc} = 1.000$, $\tau = V + H$, $\alpha_0^{tr} = \dfrac{V}{V + H}$, $q_0 = V$, k is read from Table 7-8, and p_0 is computed from the relation

$$(1 + kp_0)^2 = \frac{(1 - k)^2 \sin^2 \Theta_e - (1 + k)^2 \sin^2 \Theta_i}{\sin^2 \Theta_e - \sin^2 \Theta_i}$$

where Θ_e and Θ_i are for external and internal tangency respectively.

Adopting $k = .978$, $\alpha_0^{oc} = .532$, $\alpha_0^{tr} = .524$ from the above, and taking $\sin \Theta^{oc}(0.5) = .301$, $\sin \Theta^{tr}(0.5) = .306$ from the freehand curve data, we next inquire whether the two eclipse curves thereby determined will be consistent with the assumption of circular orbit. This is most easily done by computing the positions of the egress shoulders, that is, $\sin \Theta^{oc}(n = 0.0)$ and $\sin \Theta^{tr}(n = 0.0)$, by entering the $n = 0.00$ rows of Table 7-9 oc and 7-9 tr. We find $\sin \Theta^{oc}(0.0) = .587$ and $\sin \Theta^{tr}(0.0) = .597$ and upon spotting these on the plots $\mathfrak{I}''$ versus $\sin \Theta$, decide that (since obviously the eclipses must be of equal duration if the orbit is to be circular) the best common value is probably .597; this of course implies $\sin \Theta^{tr}(0.5) = .306$ (as we had it) but also implies $\dfrac{\sin \Theta^{oc}(0.0)}{\sin \Theta^{oc}(0.5)} = 1.952$ and therefore $\sin \Theta^{oc}(0.5) = \dfrac{.597}{1.952} = .306$ for the secondary eclipse. With this revised set of constants we interpolate in Table 7-9 for all levels listed and obtain enough points on the "computed curves" to plot them:

	Primary			Secondary		
n	$\dfrac{\sin \Theta^{tr}(n)}{\sin \Theta^{tr}(0.5)}$	$\sin \Theta^{tr}(n)$	$(1 - l^{pr})$	$\dfrac{\sin \Theta^{oc}(n)}{\sin \Theta^{oc}(0.5)}$	$\sin \Theta^{oc}(n)$	$(1 - l^{sec})$
0.00	1.954	.597	0.000	1.952	.597	0.000
0.10	1.614	.493	.036	1.613	.493	.015
0.20	1.431	.437	.073	1.431	.437	.030
0.40	1.135	.347	.146	1.135	.347	.060
0.50	1.000	.306	.182	1.000	.306	.075
0.60	.865	.264	.219	.865	.264	.090
0.80	.575	.176	.292	.575	.176	.120
0.90	.395	.121	.328	.395	.121	.135
0.95	.275	.084	.347	.276	.084	.142
0.98	.173	.053	.358	.173	.053	.147
1.00	.000	.000	.365	.000	.000	.150

(Had the eclipses been total-annular, we would have used Table 7-10 instead of 7-9.)

The two light curves are shown in Figure 7-6, below the respective "observed" and freehand curves, but in practice should be plotted on tracing paper to try for fit. The fit seems rather good, so we read off residuals $O - C$ for the normal points, group them and compute means both with regard to sign and without sign, then compute the corresponding means for the ten individuals nearest the zero of primary eclipse. We find

sin Θ	Primary		Secondary	
	Signed	Absolute	Signed	Absolute
0 to .175	−.0028	.0058	+.0030	.0055
.175 to .400	+.0021	.0067	+.0010	.0059
.400 to Θ_e	−.0092	.0119	−.0023	.0053
Over all	−.0045	.0090	+.0003	.0056
Individuals	−.0011	.0037		

We regard the solution as a satisfactory fit both as to the levels of the bottoms $(1 - l_0^{pr})$ and $(1 - l_0^{sec})$ and as to the over-all shapes of the two eclipse curves.

(3) *Reconversion for the Adopted Curve*

Since it is customary to present the adopted curve drawn in on the "original observational chart," we now have the problem of converting sets of coordinates ($\Theta, \mathfrak{J}''$) defining that adopted curve into the corresponding sets $(\theta, \Delta m'_c)$ to plot on Figure 7-1. In theory we would do this by working backward through

$$\mathfrak{J}'' = \frac{\mathfrak{J} + 0.0263 + 0.0350 \cos \theta + 0.00855 \cos 2\theta}{0.9513 - 0.03845 \cos 2\theta}$$

and then through to the magnitude difference, but in practice it is much simpler, and accurate enough for our needs, to compute, for each entry in Table 7-2, $I = \mathfrak{J} - (O - C)$ and then obtain $\Delta m'_c$ at once from Appendix Table II. In drawing the final "adopted curve" through the points $(\theta, \Delta m'_c)$ we use also the fact that sin $\Theta_e = 0.597$, obtaining from Table 7-5 (at $z = .09$), $\theta = 35°.37$ as the join of the inside-eclipse and outside-eclipse curves. The $(\theta, \Delta m'c)$ curve is shown in Figure 7-1.

(4) The System u Herculis

It is time now to bring together all the system parameters so far determined, to derive others from them, and to interpret the results. From the study of the tops we found $C_o = .0263$, $C_1 = .0350$, $C_2 = .00855$, and $z = .09$; from the study of the eclipses we found $l_0^{pr} = l_0^{tr} = .635$, $l_0^{sec} = l_0^{oc} = .850$, $k = .978$, $q_0 = .957$, $\alpha_0^{oc} = .532$, $\alpha_0^{tr} = .524$, $p_0 = -.209$, $\tau = .972$, $\sin \Theta_e = .597$, $\Theta_e = 36.°66$, and $\theta_e = 35.°37$.

By $r_g{}^2 = \dfrac{\sin^2 \Theta_e}{(1 + k)^2 - (1 + kp_0)^2 \cos^2 \Theta_e}$, $r_s = kr_g$, $L_s = \dfrac{1 - l_0^{oc}}{\alpha_0^{oc}}$,

$L_g = \dfrac{1 - l_0^{tr}}{\alpha_0^{tr} \tau}$ (checked by $L_s + L_g = 1$), $\cos i' = (1 + kp_0)r_g$, and

$\cos^2 j = (1 - z) \cos^2 i'$, we find $r_g = .319$, $r_s = .312$, $r_g + r_s = .631$, $L_s = .283$, $L_g = .717$ ($L_s + L_g = 1.000$), $\cos i' = .257$, and $\cos j = .245$. Now the r_g and r_s we obtained, are not only the radii of the two spherical components of the fictitious system we set up, but also the semimajor axes a_g and a_s of the triaxial ellipsoids of our original model, while the parameter z measures (rather indirectly!) the ellipticities of the components in their orbital plane. From $b = a \tan i' \cot j$ we find $b_g = .302$ and $b_s = .296$, the axes in the equatorial plane.

There is no way to obtain the "polar" axes directly from the light curve alone, but two simple ways exist, however, both essentially dynamical. If the ratio of the masses of the two components is known from spectroscopic work then we use $c = b - (a - b) \dfrac{1 + m_2/m_1}{3m_2/m_1}$

but if the ratio is unknown we use simply $c = \dfrac{5b - 2a}{3}$, equivalent to

the (usually reasonable) assumption that the masses are approximately equal. For u Herculis we have (as will be seen later) $\dfrac{m_2}{m_1} = .36$, so the

first formula yields $c_g = .281$ and $c_s = .276$. By $\tan i = \dfrac{a}{c} \tan i'$ we

obtain $\tan i = 4.266$ and therefore $i = 76.°8$, the inclination of the orbit plane to the "plane of the sky." Had we not known the ratio of masses, we would have obtained $i = 76.°3$, little different because the polar flattening is much more sensitive to the speed of rotation (not revolution) of the components than to their masses.

This takes care of the tidal and centrifugal effects on the shapes of the components, and leaves only the interradiation effects to consider. This is easily done: the constant $C_1 = .0350$ tells us that the hemispheres of the two components facing each other are $3\frac{1}{2}$ per cent brighter due to "reflection" than the "backs" of the stars, while the constant $C_2 = .00855$ says that the "reflection" exaggerated the light variation due to shape by a little less than 1 per cent of the unit of light, at the broadside positions of the components.

At the beginning of this study we mentioned the spectrographic orbit by Burke Smith. From 181 spectrograms he found maximum observed velocities of 95 and 265 km/sec for the two components; thus, the real orbital velocities (i.e., $\dfrac{95}{\sin i}$ and $\dfrac{265}{\sin i}$) are $v_g = 98$ and $v_s = 272$ km/sec and the velocity of the companion relative to the brighter, larger, more massive star is $v = 98 + 272 = 370$ km/sec, while the ratio of masses is $\dfrac{m_s}{m_g} = .36$ as we stated above.

But if the companion travels about the principal star at 370 km/sec and requires 2.051027 days for one trip around, then the radius of the orbit (that is, the distance between the centers of the components) is

$$R = \frac{2.051027 \times 24 \times 60 \times 60 \times 370}{2\pi} = 10,435,000 \text{ km or 7 per cent}$$

of the distance between the earth and the sun. Since a_g and a_s are .319 and .312 of the orbital radius respectively, they can now be given as 3,330,000 km and 3,260,000 km, or (better) as 4.8 and 4.7 times the sun's radius.

Now Kepler's Third Law can be expressed in a great variety of ways; for our purposes a useful form is

$$m_g + m_s = 1.04 \times 10^{-7} v^3 P$$

where m_g, m_s are masses in terms of our sun's mass while v is the relative orbital velocity in km/sec and P the orbital period in days, for our system. We find at once that $m_g + m_s = 10.8 \times$ sun's mass. But $m_s = .36$

m_g, so therefore we have $m_g = 7.9\,m_\odot$ and $m_s = 2.9\,m_\odot$. And finally, since relative mean density is relative mass divided by relative volume, we have $d_g = \dfrac{7.9}{(4.8)^3} = 7\%$ of sun's density and $d_s = \dfrac{2.9}{(4.7)^3} = 3\%$ of sun's density, very nearly.

And so our story is finished. Perhaps we should gather up all the information we have been able to derive for our system u Herculis, but instead we leave this pleasant task to the reader. We present in Figure 7-8 a drawing of the system, in scale with the sun, and we

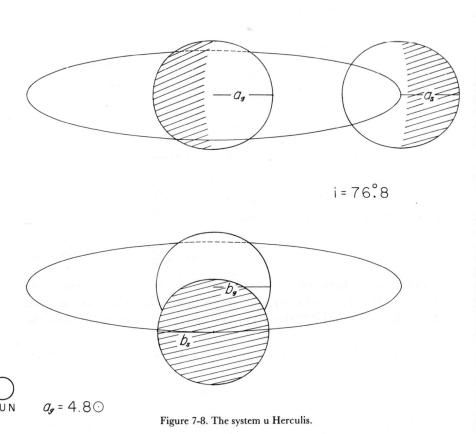

Figure 7-8. The system u Herculis.

remind the reader that all this wealth of information has been derived by study of series of planned observations on what appears (and must always appear) to *any* terrestrial observer looking through *any* telescope constructible by man, as a single point of light of varying brightness.

(The rest of the tables for Chapter 7 begin on the following page.)

Table 7-2
Normals, Ruiz' u Herculis, Blue

Normal No.	Phase (θ)	$\Delta m'$	$\mathfrak{J}$	$\cos \theta$	$\cos 2\theta$	$\mathfrak{J}''$	$\sin \Theta$	O-C
	°							
1	1.19	^{m}.725	.513	+1.000	+0.999	.638	.022	+.001
2	4.39	.683	.533	+0.997	+0.988	.660	.080	+.007
3	8.35	.621	.564	+0.989	+0.958	.692	.152	+.001
4	10.78	.552	.602	+0.982	+0.930	.732	.196	+.001
5	13.44	.516	.622	+0.973	+0.892	.752	.243	−.010
6	17.13	.394	.696	+0.956	+0.826	.830	.307	+.010
7	20.15	.327	.740	+0.939	+0.763	.874	.359	+.009
8	22.96	.264	.784	+0.921	+0.696	.918	.406	+.013
9	25.03	.241	.801	+0.906	+0.642	.933	.440	+.003
10	26.92	.218	.818	+0.892	+0.590	.948	.470	−.001
11	28.50	.207	.826	+0.879	+0.545	.954	.495	−.008
12	30.44	.188	.841	+0.862	+0.487	.967	.524	−.010
13	32.54	.178	.849	+0.843	+0.421	.971	.556	−.019
14	34.89	.143	.877	+0.820	+0.346	.997	.590	−.002
15	37.56	.134	.884	+0.793	+0.257	.999	.628	−.001
16	46.76	.082	.927	+0.685	−0.061	1.024		+.024
17	56.97	.053	.952	+0.545	−0.406	1.028		+.028
18	63.50	.037	.966	+0.446	−0.602	1.029		+.029
19	83.97	.030	.973	+0.105	−0.978	1.006		+.006
20	88.74	.030	.973	+0.022	−0.999	1.002		+.002
21	94.47	.034	.969	−0.078	−0.988	.995		−.005
22	99.83	.041	.963	−0.171	−0.942	.988		−.012
23	104.68	.040	.964	−0.253	−0.872	.989		−.011
24	107.90	.050	.955	−0.307	−0.811	.981		−.019
25	137.32	.062	.944	−0.735	+0.081	.997		−.003
26	145.61	.078	.931	−0.825	+0.362	.994	.583	−.006
27	149.19	.075	.933	−0.859	+0.475	1.000	.530	+.006
28	152.00	.108	.905	−0.883	+0.559	.974	.487	−.011
29	154.98	.116	.899	−0.906	+0.642	.970	.440	−.001
30	156.92	.133	.885	−0.920	+0.693	.957	.408	−.005
31	159.09	.150	.871	−0.934	+0.745	.944	.372	−.005
32	162.64	.158	.865	−0.954	+0.822	.940	.311	+.012
33	168.29	.212	.823	−0.979	+0.918	.898	.212	+.007
34	173.14	.232	.808	−0.993	+0.971	.884	.125	+.015
35	178.50	.272	.778	−1.000	+0.999	.852	.027	+.002
36	181.52	.274	.777	−1.000	+0.999	.851	.028	.000
37	186.93	.259	.788	−0.993	+0.971	.862	.126	−.005
38	189.84	.233	.807	−0.985	+0.942	.882	.179	−.000
39	192.62	.226	.812	−0.976	+0.905	.886	.229	−.012
40	195.74	.186	.843	−0.963	+0.853	.918	.283	−.000

Table 7-2 (continued)
Normals, Ruiz' u Herculis, Blue

Normal No.	Phase (θ)	Δm	$\mathfrak{J}$	$\cos \theta$	$\cos 2\,\theta$	$\mathfrak{J}''$	$\sin \Theta$	$O\text{-}C$
	°							
41	201.08	$^m.138$	.881	-0.933	$+0.741$	.955	.375	$+.005$
42	209.36	.086	.924	-0.872	$+0.519$	.992	.508	$+.003$
43	220.91	.069	.938	-0.756	$+0.142$	.993	.672	$-.007$
44	225.72	.057	.949	-0.698	-0.025	.998	.732	$-.002$
45	227.93	.054	.952	-0.670	-0.102	.999		$-.001$
46	230.60	.042	.962	-0.635	-0.194	1.006		$+.006$
47	234.78	.039	.965	-0.577	-0.335	1.004		$+.004$
48	238.92	.034	.969	-0.516	-0.467	1.004		$+.004$
49	242.43	.033	.970	-0.463	-0.572	1.002		$+.002$
50	250.65	.030	.973	-0.331	-0.780	1.000		.000
51	256.72	.028	.974	-0.230	-0.894	.999		$-.001$
52	259.25	.030	.973	-0.187	-0.930	.998		$-.002$
53	263.70	.036	.967	-0.110	-0.976	.992		$-.008$
54	269.00	.028	.974	-0.017	-0.999	1.001		$+.001$
55	272.94	.031	.972	$+0.051$	-0.995	1.002		$+.002$
56	276.94	.042	.962	$+0.121$	-0.971	.996		$-.004$
57	280.55	.050	.955	$+0.183$	-0.933	.992		$-.008$
58	286.63	.044	.960	$+0.286$	-0.836	1.006		$+.006$
59	296.91	.059	.947	$+0.453$	-0.590	1.010		$+.010$
60	309.48	.102	.910	$+0.636$	-0.191	.998		$-.002$
61	315.45	.114	.900	$+0.713$	$+0.016$	1.001		$+.001$
62	320.08	.126	.890	$+0.767$	$+0.176$	1.000	.660	.000
63	324.45	.161	.862	$+0.814$	$+0.324$	.979	.600	$-.021$
64	329.35	.184	.844	$+0.860$	$+0.480$	.970	.528	$-.010$
65	331.88	.231	.808	$+0.882$	$+0.556$	.935	.489	$-.025$
66	333.70	.241	.801	$+0.896$	$+0.607$	.931	.460	$-.012$
67	335.88	.285	.769	$+0.913$	$+0.666$	.900	.425	$-.019$
68	338.90	.311	.751	$+0.933$	$+0.741$	.884	.375	$+.004$
69	343.39	.429	.674	$+0.958$	$+0.837$	.806	.298	$-.006$
70	348.94	.558	.598	$+0.981$	$+0.926$	.728	.201	.000
71	352.67	.673	.538	$+0.992$	$+0.967$	.664	.134	$-.016$
72	356.55	.727	.512	$+0.998$	$+0.993$	.637	.063	$-.009$
73	358.87	.731	.510	$+1.000$	$+0.999$	.635	.021	$-.001$

Table 7-3
Individual observations near primary minimum, u Herculis

Obs. No.	Phase (θ)	$\Delta m'$	$\mathfrak{I}$	$\cos \theta$	$\cos 2\theta$	$\mathfrak{I}''$	$\sin \Theta$	O-C
305	4.39	$^m.732$	.510	0.997	0.988	.635	.0802	−.016
147	3.69	.727	.512	0.998	0.992	.637	.0675	−.010
306	3.52	.721	.515	0.992	0.992	.640	.0644	−.007
307	2.99	.737	.507	0.999	0.995	.632	.0546	−.010
148	2.64	.718	.516	0.999	0.996	.642	.0483	.000
353	2.11	.717	.517	0.999	0.997	.643	.0386	+.002
149	1.58	.743	.504	1.000	0.998	.628	.0290	−.010
308	1.06	.739	.506	1.000	0.999	.631	.0194	−.004
309	0.53	.739	.506	1.000	1.000	.631	.0098	−.003
150	0.36	.717	.517	1.000	1.000	.643	.0066	+.006
354	0.35	.719	.516	1.000	1.000	.642	.0064	+.005
151	0.88	.725	.513	1.000	1.000	.638	.0160	.000
355	1.05	.725	.513	1.000	0.999	.638	.0192	−.001
310	1.58	.733	.509	1.000	0.998	.634	.0290	−.003
152	2.11	.724	.513	0.999	0.997	.638	.0386	−.003
153	2.98	.693	.528	0.999	0.995	.655	.0544	+.008
356	4.39	.671	.539	0.997	0.988	.666	.0802	+.002
311	4.39	.688	.531	0.997	0.988	.658	.0802	+.010
312	5.09	.695	.527	0.996	0.984	.653	.0887	+.009
357	5.09	.670	.540	0.996	0.984	.667	.0887	−.002

Table 7-4
For derivation of A_0, A_1, A_2, for u Herculis

θ	a	b	$\frac{a-b}{2}$	$\cos \theta$	$\frac{a+b}{2}$	$\cos 2\theta$
30	0.835	0.917	−0.041	0.866	0.876	+0.500
35	0.870	0.932	−0.031	0.819	0.901	+0.342
40	0.893	0.943	−0.025	0.766	0.918	+0.174
45	0.909	0.952	−0.022	0.707	0.930	0.000
50	0.924	0.959	−0.018	0.643	0.942	−0.174
55	0.936	0.963	−0.014	0.574	0.950	−0.342
60	0.946	0.967	−0.010	0.500	0.956	−0.500
65	0.954	0.969	−0.008	0.423	0.962	−0.643
70	0.960	0.970	−0.005	0.342	0.965	−0.766
75	0.965	0.971	−0.003	0.259	0.968	−0.866
80	0.968	0.972	−0.002	0.174	0.970	−0.940
85	0.970	0.972	−0.001	0.087	0.971	−0.985
90	0.971	0.971	0.000	0.000	0.971	−1.000

Table 7-5
$Sin\ \Theta\ (z, \theta)$

θ	$z = .00$	.05	.10	.15	.20	.25
00	.000	.000	.000	.000	.000	.000
01	.017	.018	.018	.019	.020	.020
02	.035	.036	.037	.038	.039	.040
03	.052	.054	.055	.057	.058	.060
04	.070	.072	.074	.076	.078	.080
05	.087	.089	.092	.094	.097	.101
06	.105	.107	.110	.113	.117	.120
07	.122	.125	.128	.132	.136	.140
08	.139	.143	.147	.151	.155	.160
09	.156	.160	.165	.169	.174	.180
10	.174	.178	.183	.188	.193	.200
11	.191	.196	.201	.206	.212	.219
12	.208	.213	.219	.225	.231	.238
13	.225	.230	.236	.243	.250	.258
14	.242	.248	.254	.261	.269	.277
15	.259	.265	.272	.279	.287	.296
16	.276	.282	.289	.297	.305	.314
17	.292	.299	.307	.315	.323	.333
18	.309	.316	.324	.332	.341	.351
19	.326	.333	.341	.350	.359	.369
20	.342	.350	.358	.367	.377	.387
21	.358	.366	.375	.384	.394	.405
22	.375	.383	.392	.401	.412	.423
23	.391	.399	.408	.418	.429	.440
24	.407	.416	.425	.435	.446	.457
25	.423	.432	.441	.451	.462	.474
26	.438	.447	.457	.468	.479	.491
27	.454	.463	.473	.484	.495	.507
28	.469	.479	.489	.500	.511	.523
29	.485	.494	.504	.515	.527	.539
30	.500	.510	.520	.531	.542	.555
31	.515	.525	.535	.546	.558	.570
32	.530	.540	.550	.561	.573	.585
33	.545	.554	.565	.576	.588	.600
34	.559	.569	.579	.590	.602	.614
35	.574	.583	.594	.605	.616	.629
36	.588	.598	.608	.619	.630	.643
37	.602	.612	.622	.633	.644	.656
38	.616	.625	.636	.647	.658	.670
39	.629	.639	.649	.660	.671	.683
40	.643	.652	.663	.673	.684	.696
41	.656	.666	.676	.686	.697	.708
42	.669	.679	.689	.699	.709	.721
43	.682	.691	.701	.711	.722	.733
44	.695	.704	.713	.723	.734	.744
45	.707	.716	.725	.735	.745	.756

Table 7-6 oc

Sin $\Theta_{0.8}^{oc}$/sin Θ_n^{oc}

For occultation eclipses partial at deepest phase

n	α_o^{oc}	$k = 1.00$	.90	.80	.70	.60	.50	.40	
0.2	40	.414	.418	.423	.428	.433	.438	.444	40
0.4		.517	.521	.525	.528	.533	.537	.541	
0.6		.672	.675	.678	.680	.682	.685	.687	
0.9		1.446	1.444	1.441	1.439	1.437	1.434	1.432	
	50	.404	.411	.418	.424	.431	.438	.444	50
		.509	.515	.520	.526	.531	.536	.541	
		.666	.671	.675	.678	.681	.685	.688	
		1.452	1.448	1.444	1.440	1.437	1.433	1.430	
	60	.393	.403	.412	.421	.430	.438	.446	60
		.499	.508	.515	.522	.530	.537	.543	
		.659	.666	.671	.676	.681	.686	.689	
		1.462	1.455	1.448	1.442	1.437	1.432	1.428	
	70	.379	.392	.405	.418	.429	.440	.451	70
		.486	.498	.510	.520	.529	.539	.548	
		.650	.659	.667	.675	.681	.687	.692	
		1.477	1.465	1.454	1.445	1.437	1.430	1.424	
	80	.359	.379	.398	.415	.430	.444	.457	80
		.466	.486	.503	.518	.531	.543	.554	
		.634	.650	.663	.674	.683	.691	.698	
		1.499	1.478	1.460	1.446	1.434	1.424	1.416	
	90	.330	.362	.389	.413	.434	.453	.470	90
		.436	.470	.496	.518	.536	.553	.567	
		.607	.637	.658	.674	.687	.698	.708	
		1.557	1.503	1.466	1.441	1.422	1.407	1.395	
	95	.307	.352	.387	.415	.440	.463	.483	95
		.412	.459	.493	.520	.543	.563	.580	
		.585	.628	.656	.677	.694	.707	.719	
		1.625	1.521	1.466	1.431	1.405	1.386	1.372	
	100	.276	.341	.391	.432	.467	.498	.525	100
		.374	.448	.500	.540	.572	.599	.621	
		.545	.619	.664	.696	.720	.739	.754	
		1.818	1.523	1.418	1.363	1.329	1.306	1.288	

Table 7-6 oc (continued)
$$\text{Sin } \Theta_{0.8}^{oc}/\sin \Theta_n^{oc}$$

For occultation eclipses total at deepest phase

(Note that the vertical argument in this table is α_o^{tr}, "brought over" from the other eclipse.)

n	α_o^{tr}	$k = 1.00$	.90	.80	.70	.60	.50	.40	
0.2	100	.276	.341	.391	.432	.467	.498	.525	100
0.4		.374	.448	.500	.540	.572	.599	.621	
0.6		.545	.619	.664	.696	.720	.739	.754	
0.9		1.818	1.523	1.418	1.363	1.329	1.306	1.288	
	1.05					.520	.552	.572	1.05
						.626	.652	.666	
						.767	.783	.787	
						1.219	1.205	1.176	
	1.10						.600	.628	1.10
							.699	.720	
							.820	.832	
							1.149	1.140	
	1.15							.670	1.15
								.758	
								.860	
								1.109	

Central total, $\alpha_o^{tr} = \alpha_c^{tr}$

n		$k = 1.00$	.90	.80	.70	.60	.50	.40
0.2		.276	.348	.416	.482	.548	.615	.684
0.4		.374	.456	.528	.593	.654	.713	.770
0.6		.545	.628	.691	.743	.789	.830	.867
0.9		1.818	1.479	1.331	1.241	1.182	1.135	1.098
	α_c^{tr}	1.000	1.009	1.025	1.048	1.078	1.117	1.168

Table 7-6 tr
$$\text{Sin } \Theta_{0.8}^{tr}/\sin \Theta_n^{tr}$$

For transit eclipses partial at deepest phase

n	α_o^{tr}	$k = 1.00$	.90	.80	.70	.60	.50	.40	
0.2	.40	.414	.415	.417	.421	.425	.430	.435	.40
0.4		.517	.517	.519	.522	.526	.530	.534	
0.6		.672	.673	.674	.676	.678	.680	.683	
0.9		1.446	1.445	1.444	1.442	1.441	1.438	1.435	
	.50	.404	.406	.410	.415	.421	.427	.434	.50
		.509	.510	.513	.517	.522	.528	.533	
		.666	.668	.670	.673	.676	.679	.683	
		1.452	1.450	1.448	1.445	1.442	1.439	1.436	
	.60	.393	.396	.401	.408	.416	.424	.433	.60
		.499	.501	.506	.512	.518	.525	.533	
		.659	.661	.664	.668	.673	.678	.682	
		1.462	1.458	1.454	1.449	1.444	1.439	1.435	
	.70	.379	.383	.390	.400	.411	.422	.433	.70
		.486	.490	.496	.505	.514	.523	.533	
		.650	.653	.658	.664	.671	.677	.683	
		1.477	1.471	1.463	1.454	1.446	1.439	1.433	
	.80	.359	.366	.378	.392	.406	.421	.435	.80
		.466	.473	.485	.498	.511	.523	.535	
		.634	.640	.650	.660	.669	.677	.685	
		1.499	1.489	1.477	1.463	1.450	1.439	1.430	
	.90	.330	.343	.363	.384	.403	.422	.439	.90
		.436	.450	.472	.491	.509	.525	.540	
		.607	.622	.640	.655	.668	.679	.689	
		1.557	1.524	1.492	1.466	1.448	1.433	1.422	
	.95	.307	.329	.355	.380	.403	.424	.444	.95
		.412	.435	.464	.488	.510	.529	.546	
		.585	.608	.633	.653	.670	.683	.694	
		1.625	1.553	1.500	1.464	1.440	1.423	1.409	
	1.00	.276	.312	.349	.381	.410	.435	.457	1.00
		.374	.417	.458	.491	.518	.541	.560	
		.545	.592	.630	.657	.678	.694	.707	
		1.818	1.587	1.487	1.439	1.410	1.392	1.376	

Table 7-6 tr (continued)
$$\text{Sin } \Theta^{tr}_{0.8}/\text{sin } \Theta^{tr}_{n}$$
For transit eclipses annular at deepest phase

n	α_o^{tr}	$k = 1.00$	.90	.80	.70	.60	.50	.40	
0.2	1.00	.276	.312	.349	.381	.410	.435	.457	1.00
0.4		.374	.417	.458	.491	.518	.541	.560	
0.6		.545	.592	.630	.657	.678	.694	.707	
0.9		1.818	1.587	1.487	1.439	1.410	1.392	1.376	
	1.05					.447	.474	.498	1.05
						.560	.583	.602	
						.718	.732	.744	
						1.294	1.289	1.283	
	1.10						.516	.540	1.10
							.625	.644	
							.768	.778	
							1.230	1.231	
	1.15							.579	1.15
								.681	
								.806	
								1.256	

Central annular, $\alpha_o^{tr} = \alpha_c^{tr}$

n		$k = 1.00$	.90	.80	.70	.60	.50	.40	
0.2		.276	.314	.362	.415	.471	.530	.592	
0.4		.374	.420	.474	.530	.585	.639	.692	
0.6		.545	.595	.648	.697	.740	.779	.815	
0.9		1.818	1.553	1.400	1.309	1.251	1.228	1.271	
	α_c^{tr}	1.000	1.009	1.025	1.048	1.078	1.117	1.168	

Table 7-7
τ (k)

k	τ	k	τ	k	τ
100	.100	80	.694	60	.393
99	.988	79	.678	59	.380
98	.975	78	.662	58	.367
97	.962	77	.646	57	.354
96	.948	76	.630	56	.341
95	.933	75	.615	55	.329
94	.918	74	.599	54	.316
93	.903	73	.583	53	.304
92	.888	72	.568	52	.292
91	.872	71	.552	51	.280
90	.856	70	.537	50	.269
89	.840	69	.522	49	.258
88	.824	68	.507	48	.247
87	.808	67	.492	47	.236
86	.792	66	.478	46	.225
85	.776	65	.463	45	.215
84	.759	64	.449	44	.205
83	.743	63	.435	43	.195
82	.727	62	.421	42	.185
81	.711	61	.407	41	.176
				40	.167

Table 7-8
$k(q_o, \alpha_o^{oc})$ for partial eclipses

α_o^{oc}	$q_o = 1.00$	.90	.80	.70	.60	.50	.40	.30	.20	.10
.40	1.000	.951	.899	.844	.786	.722	.651	.570	.473	.344
.50	1.000	.950	.897	.842	.783	.719	.648	.567	.470	.342
.60	1.000	.949	.895	.839	.779	.715	.644	.563	.467	.340
.70	.000	.947	.892	.835	.775	.710	.639	.559	.463	.337
.80	1.000	.944	.888	.830	.769	.704	.633	.553	.458	.333
.90	1.000	.940	.882	.823	.761	.696	.625	.545	.451	.328
.95	1.000	.937	.877	.817	.755	.689	.618	.539	.446	.324
1.00	1.000	.928	.865	.803	.741	.675	.605	.527	.435	.316

$p_o(q_o, \alpha_o^{oc})$ for partial eclipses

α_o^{oc}	$q_o = 1.00$	.90	.80	.70	.60	.50	.40	.30	.20	.10
.40	−.004	+.005	+.013	+.022	+.032	+.042	+.052	+.064	+.078	+.097
.50	−.163	−.152	−.142	−.132	−.121	−.110	−.098	−.085	−.069	−.050
.60	−.317	−.305	−.293	−.281	−.269	−.257	−.244	−.230	−.214	−.195
.70	−.471	−.456	−.442	−.429	−.416	−.403	−.390	−.377	−.361	−.342
.80	−.628	−.610	−.595	−.582	−.569	−.556	−.543	−.530	−.516	−.499
.90	−.795	−.775	−.760	−.747	−.736	−.725	−.715	−.704	−.692	−.679
.95	−.888	−.868	−.854	−.844	−.835	−.826	−.818	−.810	−.802	−.792
1.00	−1.000	−1.000	−1.000	−1.000	−1.000	−1.000	−1.000	−1.000	−1.000	−1.000

Table 7-9 oc
Sin $\Theta^{oc}(k, \alpha_o^{oc}, n)/\sin \Theta^{oc}(k, \alpha_o^{oc}, n = 0.50)$

For occultation eclipses partial at deepest phase

n	α_o^{oc}	$k = 1.00$	.90	.80	.70	.60	.50	.40	
0.00	.40	1.900	1.878	1.856	1.833	1.810	1.786	1.761	.40
0.10		1.584	1.572	1.559	1.546	1.534	1.520	1.506	
0.20		1.412	1.404	1.396	1.387	1.379	1.371	1.362	
0.40		1.130	1.128	1.126	1.124	1.122	1.120	1.118	
0.50		1.000	1.000	1.000	1.000	1.000	1.000	1.000	
0.60		.869	.871	.872	.874	.876	.877	.879	
0.80		.584	.587	.591	.594	.597	.601	.604	
0.90		.404	.406	.409	.412	.416	.418	.421	
0.95		.282	.285	.287	.289	.292	.294	.297	
0.98		.177	.179	.181	.182	.184	.185	.187	
1.00		.000	.000	.000	.000	.000	.000	.000	
	.50	1.943	1.913	1.883	1.853	1.823	1.792	1.762	.50
		1.608	1.591	1.574	1.557	1.540	1.522	1.505	
		1.427	1.416	1.405	1.394	1.383	1.372	1.361	
		1.134	1.131	1.129	1.126	1.123	1.120	1.117	
		1.000	1.000	1.000	1.000	1.000	1.000	1.000	
		.866	.868	.871	.873	.875	.877	.879	
		.577	.582	.587	.592	.596	.601	.605	
		.397	.401	.406	.410	.415	.419	.423	
		.277	.281	.284	.288	.291	.294	.297	
		.174	.176	.179	.181	.183	.186	.188	
		.000	.000	.000	.000	.000	.000	.000	
	.60	1.993	1.951	1.911	1.872	1.834	1.796	1.759	.60
		1.636	1.612	1.589	1.567	1.545	1.523	1.503	
		1.446	1.430	1.415	1.400	1.386	1.372	1.359	
		1.139	1.135	1.131	1.127	1.123	1.120	1.116	
		1.000	1.000	1.000	1.000	1.000	1.000	1.000	
		.862	.865	.869	.872	.875	.877	.880	
		.568	.576	.583	.589	.596	.602	.607	
		.389	.395	.402	.408	.415	.420	.425	
		.270	.276	.281	.286	.291	.295	.299	
		.169	.173	.176	.180	.183	.186	.189	
		.000	.000	.000	.000	.000	.000	.000	
	.70	2.052	1.995	1.941	1.891	1.843	1.797	1.753	.70
		1.671	1.637	1.606	1.577	1.549	1.523	1.497	
		1.469	1.447	1.426	1.406	1.388	1.371	1.355	
		1.146	1.140	1.134	1.129	1.124	1.119	1.115	
		1.000	1.000	1.000	1.000	1.000	1.000	1.000	
		.857	.862	.867	.871	.875	.878	.881	
		.557	.568	.578	.587	.595	.603	.610	
		.377	.387	.397	.406	.415	.422	.429	
		.260	.269	.277	.284	.291	.297	.302	
		.162	.169	.174	.179	.183	.187	.191	
		.000	.000	.000	.000	.000	.000	.000	

Table 7-9 oc (continued)
Sin $\Theta^{oc}(k, \alpha_o^{oc}, n)$/sin $\Theta^{oc}(k, \alpha_o^{oc}, n = 0.50)$

For occultation eclipses partial at deepest phase

n	α_o^{tr}	$k = 1.00$	.90	.80	.70	.60	.50	.40	
0.00	.80	2.127	2.047	1.975	1.909	1.849	1.793	1.741	
0.10		1.716	1.668	1.625	1.586	1.551	1.519	1.488	
0.20		1.499	1.467	1.438	1.412	1.389	1.368	1.348	
0.40		1.155	1.146	1.138	1.130	1.124	1.118	1.113	
0.50		1.000	1.000	1.000	1.000	1.000	1.000	1.000	
0.60		.849	.857	.864	.870	.875	.880	.884	
0.80		.539	.557	.572	.586	.597	.607	.616	
0.90		.359	.377	.392	.405	.417	.427	.436	
0.95		.246	.261	.273	.284	.293	.301	.309	
0.98		.152	.162	.171	.178	.185	.191	.195	
1.00		.000	.000	.000	.000	.000	.000	.000	
	.90	2.229	2.111	2.012	1.926	1.849	1.780	1.718	.90
		1.780	1.707	1.646	1.594	1.549	1.509	1.472	
		1.543	1.493	1.452	1.417	1.387	1.360	1.336	
		1.167	1.153	1.141	1.131	1.123	1.116	1.109	
		1.000	1.000	1.000	1.000	1.000	1.000	1.000	
		.838	.850	.860	.869	.876	.882	.888	
		.509	.541	.566	.586	.602	.616	.628	
		.327	.361	.386	.406	.423	.438	.451	
		.218	.247	.268	.286	.300	.312	.322	
		.132	.153	.168	.180	.190	.199	.206	
		.000	.000	.000	.000	.000	.000	.000	
	.95	2.297	2.149	2.031	1.930	1.843	1.766	1.698	.95
		1.823	1.731	1.657	1.596	1.544	1.498	1.458	
		1.573	1.509	1.459	1.418	1.383	1.352	1.326	
		1.177	1.158	1.143	1.131	1.121	1.113	1.105	
		1.000	1.000	1.000	1.000	1.000	1.000	1.000	
		.829	.846	.859	.869	.878	.885	.892	
		.485	.531	.563	.588	.609	.626	.641	
		.298	.349	.385	.412	.434	.452	.467	
		.191	.238	.269	.292	.310	.326	.339	
		.112	.146	.168	.185	.199	.211	.221	
		.000	.000	.000	.000	.000	.000	.000	
	1.00	2.389	2.191	2.037	1.911	1.807	1.718	1.642	1.00
		1.882	1.756	1.659	1.582	1.518	1.464	1.418	
		1.614	1.526	1.460	1.407	1.364	1.328	1.297	
		1.190	1.163	1.143	1.127	1.114	1.104	1.095	
		1.000	1.000	1.000	1.000	1.000	1.000	1.000	
		.816	.841	.860	.874	.885	.895	.903	
		.445	.521	.571	.608	.637	.661	.680	
		.245	.342	.402	.446	.480	.506	.528	
		.134	.231	.295	.337	.369	.395	.417	
		.0588	.153	.204	.240	.268	.290	.308	
		.000	.000	.000	.000	.000	.000	.000	

Table 7-9 tr

Sin $\Theta^{tr}(k, \alpha_o^{tr}, n)$/sin $\Theta^{tr}(k, \alpha_o^{tr}, n = 0.50)$

For transit eclipses partial at deepest phase

n	α_o^{tr}	$k = 1.00$	.90	.80	.70	.60	.50	.40	
0.00	.40	1.900	1.895	1.883	1.864	1.841	1.814	1.784	.40
0.10		1.584	1.582	1.575	1.566	1.554	1.540	1.524	
0.20		1.412	1.410	1.406	1.400	1.392	1.384	1.374	
0.40		1.130	1.130	1.129	1.127	1.125	1.123	1.121	
0.50		1.000	1.000	1.000	1.000	1.000	1.000	1.000	
0.60		.869	.870	.871	.872	.873	.875	.877	
0.80		.584	.585	.586	.589	.592	.595	.599	
0.90		.404	.404	.406	.407	.410	.414	.417	
0.95		.282	.282	.284	.285	.288	.290	.293	
0.98		.177	.178	.179	.180	.181	.183	.184	
1.00		.000	.000	.000	.000	.000	.000	.000	
	.50	1.943	1.937	1.920	1.895	1.866	1.832	1.795	.50
		1.608	1.605	1.596	1.583	1.567	1.549	1.529	
		1.427	1.425	1.419	1.411	1.401	1.389	1.377	
		1.134	1.134	1.132	1.130	1.127	1.125	1.122	
		1.000	1.000	1.000	1.000	1.000	1.000	1.000	
		.866	.867	.868	.869	.871	.874	.876	
		.577	.579	.581	.585	.589	.593	.598	
		.397	.398	.401	.404	.407	.412	.416	
		.277	.278	.280	.282	.285	.289	.292	
		.174	.175	.176	.178	.180	.182	.184	
		.000	.000	.000	.000	.000	.000	.000	
	.60	1.993	1.984	1.960	1.928	1.891	1.849	1.805	
		1.636	1.632	1.619	1.601	1.580	1.557	1.533	
		1.446	1.443	1.434	1.422	1.409	1.395	1.379	
		1.139	1.138	1.136	1.133	1.130	1.126	1.122	
		1.000	1.000	1.000	1.000	1.000	1.000	1.000	
		.862	.863	.865	.867	.870	.873	.876	
		.568	.571	.575	.580	.586	.592	.597	
		.389	.391	.395	.400	.405	.411	.416	
		.270	.272	.275	.279	.283	.288	.292	
		.169	.170	.172	.175	.178	.181	.184	
		.000	.000	.000	.000	.000	.000	.000	
	.70	2.052	2.039	2.006	1.964	1.916	1.865	1.812	.70
		1.671	1.664	1.645	1.620	1.593	1.565	1.537	
		1.469	1.464	1.451	1.435	1.418	1.400	1.381	
		1.146	1.144	1.141	1.137	1.132	1.127	1.122	
		1.000	1.000	1.000	1.000	1.000	1.000	1.000	
		.857	.858	.861	.865	.868	.872	.876	
		.557	.561	.567	.574	.582	.590	.598	
		.377	.381	.387	.395	.402	.410	.417	
		.260	.263	.269	.275	.281	.287	.293	
		.162	.164	.168	.172	.177	.181	.185	
		.000	.000	.000	.000	.000	.000	.000	

Table 7-9 tr (continued)
$$\text{Sin } \Theta^{tr}(k, \alpha_o^{tr}, n)/\text{sin } \Theta^{tr}(k, \alpha_o^{tr}, n = 0.50)$$

For transit eclipses partial at deepest phase

n	α_o^{tr}	$k = 1.00$	.90	.80	.70	.60	.50	.40	
0.00	.80	2.127	2.106	2.059	2.002	1.941	1.879	1.816	.80
0.10		1.716	1.704	1.676	1.642	1.607	1.572	1.538	
0.20		1.499	1.491	1.472	1.450	1.427	1.404	1.381	
0.40		1.155	1.152	1.147	1.141	1.134	1.128	1.122	
0.50		1.000	1.000	1.000	1.000	1.000	1.000	1.000	
0.60		.849	.851	.856	.862	.867	.872	.876	
0.80		.539	.545	.557	.568	.579	.590	.600	
0.90		.359	.366	.377	.389	.400	.410	.420	
0.95		.246	.251	.261	.270	.279	.287	.295	
0.98		.152	.157	.163	.169	.176	.181	.186	
1.00		.000	.000	.000	.000	.000	.000	.000	
	.90	2.229	2.193	2.122	2.044	1.965	1.888	1.815	.90
		1.780	1.756	1.713	1.666	1.620	1.576	1.535	
		1.543	1.526	1.497	1.465	1.434	1.405	1.378	
		1.167	1.162	1.154	1.145	1.136	1.128	1.121	
		1.000	1.000	1.000	1.000	1.000	1.000	1.000	
		.838	.843	.850	.858	.865	.872	.877	
		.509	.523	.544	.562	.578	.592	.605	
		.327	.344	.365	.383	.399	.414	.426	
		.218	.233	.251	.266	.280	.291	.301	
		.132	.144	.156	.167	.176	.184	.191	
		.000	.000	.000	.000	.000	.000	.000	
	.95	2.297	2.245	2.158	2.065	1.975	1.889	1.809	.95
		1.823	1.789	1.734	1.678	1.625	1.575	1.530	
		1.573	1.549	1.511	1.473	1.437	1.404	1.374	
		1.177	1.169	1.158	1.146	1.136	1.127	1.119	
		1.000	1.000	1.000	1.000	1.000	1.000	1.000	
		.829	.837	.847	.857	.865	.873	.879	
		.485	.509	.536	.560	.580	.596	.611	
		.298	.328	.357	.382	.402	.420	.434	
		.191	.219	.246	.267	.284	.297	.309	
		.112	.134	.153	.168	.180	.189	.197	
		.000	.000	.000	.000	.000	.000	.000	
	1.00	2.389	2.305	2.191	2.079	1.975	1.879	1.792	1.00
		1.882	1.827	1.754	1.685	1.623	1.567	1.517	
		1.614	1.574	1.524	1.477	1.435	1.398	1.365	
		1.190	1.177	1.161	1.147	1.135	1.125	1.116	
		1.000	1.000	1.000	1.000	1.000	1.000	1.000	
		.816	.829	.844	.857	.867	.876	.883	
		.445	.491	.532	.563	.588	.608	.624	
		.245	.309	.357	.391	.417	.437	.454	
		.134	.206	.251	.281	.303	.319	.333	
		.0588	.128	.163	.185	.200	.212	.222	
		.000	.000	.000	.000	.000	.000	.000	

Table 7-10 oc

$$\text{Sin } \Theta^{oc}(k, \alpha_o^{tr}, n^{oc})/\text{sin } \Theta^{oc}(k, \alpha_o^{tr}, n^{oc} = -0.50)$$

For occultation eclipses total at deepest phase

(Note that the vertical argument in this table is α_o^{tr}, "brought over" from the other eclipse.)

n^{oc}	α_o^{tr}	$k = 1.00$	.90	.80	.70	.60	.50	.40	
0.00	1.00	2.389	2.191	2.037	1.911	1.807	1.718	1.642	1.00
0.10		1.882	1.756	1.659	1.582	1.518	1.464	1.418	
0.20		1.614	1.526	1.460	1.407	1.364	1.328	1.297	
0.40		1.190	1.163	1.143	1.127	1.114	1.104	1.095	
0.50		1.000	1.000	1.000	1.000	1.000	1.000	1.000	
0.60		.816	.841	.860	.874	.885	.895	.903	
0.80		.445	.521	.571	.608	.637	.661	.680	
0.90		.245	.342	.402	.446	.480	.506	.528	
0.95		.134	.231	.295	.337	.369	.395	.417	
0.98		.0588	.153	.204	.240	.268	.290	.308	
1.00		.000	.000	.000	.000	.000	.000	.000	
	1.05					1.732	1.646	1.572	1.05
						1.467	1.415	1.370	
						1.326	1.291	1.261	
						1.102	1.092	1.083	
						1.000	1.000	1.000	
						.900	.909	.916	
						.690	.712	.721	
						.566	.591	.613	
						.488	.512	.532	
						.425	.445	.464	
						.343	.353	.364	
	1.10						1.578	1.508	1.10
							1.369	1.327	
							1.258	1.230	
							1.080	1.072	
							1.000	1.000	
							.921	.928	
							.755	.772	
							.657	.677	
							.596	.616	
							.548	.566	
							.486	.499	
	1.15							1.452	1.15
								1.289	
								1.202	
								1.063	
								1.000	
								.937	
								.806	
								.727	
								.678	
								.639	
								.588	

Table 7-10 oc (continued)
$$\text{Sin } \Theta^{oc}(k, \alpha_o^{tr}, n^{oc})/\sin \Theta^{oc}(k, \alpha_o^{tr}, n^{oc} = 0.50)$$

For occultation eclipses total at deepest phase

(Note that the vertical argument in this table is α_o^{tr}, "brought over" from the other eclipse.)

n^{oc}	α_o^{tr}	$k = 1.00$	.90	.80	.70	.60	.50	.40
				Central total, $\alpha_o^{tr} = \alpha_c^{tr}$				
0.00		2.389	2.179	1.998	1.837	1.691	1.558	1.434
0.10		1.882	1.748	1.633	1.531	1.439	1.355	1.277
0.20		1.614	1.521	1.440	1.370	1.306	1.248	1.193
0.40		1.190	1.161	1.136	1.114	1.095	1.077	1.060
0.50		1.000	1.000	1.000	1.000	1.000	1.000	1.000
0.60		.816	.844	.868	.889	.907	.925	.941
0.80		.445	.530	.600	.660	.715	.767	.816
0.90		.245	.358	.452	.532	.606	.676	.743
0.95		.134	.261	.364	.455	.539	.620	.697
0.98		.102	.223	.325	.418	.506	.591	.674
1.00		.000	.115	.222	.324	.423	.519	.614
	α_c^{tr}	1.000	1.009	1.025	1.048	1.078	1.117	1.168

$$\text{Sin } \Theta^{oc}(k, \alpha_o^{tr}, n_i^{oc} = 1)/\sin \Theta^{oc}(k, \alpha_o^{tr}, n^{oc} = 0.50)$$

For occultation eclipses total at deepest phase

(Note that the vertical argument in this table is α_o^{tr}, "brought over" from the other eclipse.)

α_o^{tr}	$k = 1.00$	.90	.80	.70	.60	.50	.40	
1.00	.000	.000	.000	.000	.000	.000	.000	1.00
1.01			.137	.146	.153	.160	.165	1.01
1.02			.197	.208	.217	.225	.233	1.02
1.03				.256	.266	.275	.285	1.03
1.04				.296	.307	.317	.328	1.04
1.05					.343	.353	.364	1.05
1.06					.374	.385	.397	1.06
1.07					.403	.414	.426	1.07
1.08						.440	.452	1.08
1.09						.464	.476	1.09
1.10						.486	.499	1.10
1.11						.507	.519	1.11
1.12							.538	1.12
1.13							.556	1.13
1.14							.573	1.14
1.15							.588	1.15
1.16							.603	1.16
			Central total, $\alpha_o^{tr} = \alpha_c^{tr}$					
	.000	.115	.222	.324	.423	.519	.614	
α_c^{tr}	1.000	1.009	1.025	1.048	1.078	1.117	1.168	

Table 7-10 tr

Sin $\Theta^{tr}(k, \alpha_o^{tr}, n)$/sin $\Theta^{tr}(k, \alpha_o^{tr}, n = 0.50)$

For transit eclipses annular at deepest phase

n	α_o^{tr}	$k = 1.00$	.90	.80	.70	.60	.50	.40	
0.00	1.00	2.389	2.305	2.191	2.079	1.975	1.879	1.792	1.00
0.10		1.882	1.827	1.754	1.685	1.623	1.567	1.517	
0.20		1.614	1.574	1.524	1.477	1.435	1.398	1.365	
0.40		1.190	1.177	1.161	1.147	1.135	1.125	1.116	
0.50		1.000	1.000	1.000	1.000	1.000	1.000	1.000	
0.60		.816	.829	.844	.857	.867	.876	.883	
0.80		.445	.491	.532	.563	.588	.608	.624	
0.90		.245	.309	.357	.391	.417	.437	.454	
0.95		.134	.206	.251	.281	.303	.319	.333	
0.98		.0588	.128	.163	.185	.200	.212	.222	
1.00		.000	.000	.000	.000	.000	.000	.000	
	1.05					1.926	1.826	1.737	1.05
						1.588	1.530	1.478	
						1.409	1.370	1.336	
						1.126	1.115	1.106	
						1.000	1.000	1.000	
						.878	.887	.894	
						.630	.650	.666	
						.487	.504	.519	
						.388	.399	.410	
						.254	.261	.268	
						.000	.000	.000	
	1.10						1.767	1.678	1.10
							1.488	1.437	
							1.339	1.306	
							1.105	1.095	
							1.000	1.000	
							.899	.906	
							.690	.705	
							.561	.573	
							.418	.425	
							.269	.273	
							.000	.000	
	1.15							1.620	1.15
								1.397	
								1.277	
								1.086	
								1.000	
								.916	
								.739	
								.588	
								.429	
								.275	
								.000	

Table 7-10 tr (continued)

$$\text{Sin } \Theta^{tr}(k, \alpha_o^{t'}, n)/\text{sin } \Theta^{tr}(k, \alpha_o^{tr}, n = 0.50)$$

For transit eclipses annular at deepest phase

n	α_o^{tr}	$k = 1.00$	.90	.80	.70	.60	.50	.40
				Central annular, $\alpha_o^{tr} = \alpha_c^{tr}$				
0.00		2.389	2.309	2.182	2.041	1.894	1.747	1.600
0.10		1.882	1.828	1.747	1.657	1.565	1.473	1.383
0.20		1.614	1.575	1.518	1.455	1.392	1.329	1.267
0.40		1.190	1.177	1.158	1.139	1.120	1.101	1.083
0.50		1.000	1.000	1.000	1.000	1.000	1.000	1.000
0.60		.816	.830	.848	.867	.885	.903	.920
0.80		.445	.494	.550	.604	.655	.704	.750
0.90		.245	.318	.392	.462	.523	.573	.590
0.95		.134	.223	.303	.371	.403	.420	.430
0.98		.0588	.156	.221	.244	.262	.271	.276
1.00		.000	.000	.000	.000	.000	.000	.000
	α_c^{tr}	1.009	1.009	1.025	1.048	1.078	1.117	1.168

$$\text{Sin } \Theta^{tr}(k, \alpha_o^{tr}, n_i = 1/\alpha_o^{tr})/\text{sin } \Theta^{tr}(k, \alpha_o^{tr}, n = 0.50)$$

For transit eclipses annular at deepest phase

α_o^{tr}	$k = 1.00$	.90	.80	.70	.60	.50	.40	
1.00	0.000	0.000	0.000	0.000	0.000	0.000	0.000	1.00
1.01			.149	.160	.168	.175	.181	1.01
1.02			.214	.229	.240	.249	.256	1.02
1.03				.282	.294	.304	.314	1.03
1.04				.328	.340	.351	.362	1.04
1.05					.381	.392	.403	1.05
1.06					.417	.428	.439	1.06
1.07					.450	.461	.472	1.07
1.08						.491	.502	1.08
1.09						.519	.530	1.09
1.10						.544	.555	1.10
1.11						.568	.578	1.11
1.12							.600	1.12
1.13							.620	1.13
1.14							.639	1.14
1.15							.657	1.15
1.16							.673	1.16

Central annular, $\alpha_o^{tr} = \alpha_c^{tr}$

	.000	.122	.242	.360	.473	.582	.686
α_c^{tr}	1.000	1.009	1.025	1.048	1.078	1.117	1.168
n_i	1.000	.991	.976	.954	.928	.895	.856

Appendix Table I
Julian Days of Jan. 0 for years 1960–2009

	0	1	2	3	4	5	6	7	8	9
1960+	36934	37300	37665	38030	38395	38761	39126	39491	39856	40222
1970+	40587	40952	41317	41683	42048	42413	42778	43144	43509	43874
1980+	44239	44605	44970	45335	45700	46066	46431	46796	47161	47527
1990+	47892	48257	48622	48988	49353	49718	50083	50449	50814	51179
2000+	51544	51909	52274	52639	53004	53370	53735	54100	54465	54831

JD = 240 0000 + number in Table. Note that Julian Days begin at noon.

Appendix Table II
Conversion of difference of magnitude to relative intensity

Δm	0	1	2	3	4	5	6	7	8	9	Δm
0.00	1.0000	.9991	.9982	.9972	.9963	.9954	.9945	.9936	.9927	.9917	0.00
.01	9908	9899	9890	9881	9872	9863	9854	9845	9836	9827	.01
.02	9817	9808	9799	9790	9781	9772	9763	9754	9745	9736	.02
.03	9727	9719	9710	9701	9692	9683	9674	9665	9656	9647	.03
.04	9638	9629	9621	9612	9603	9594	.9585	9576	9568	9559	.04
.05	9550	9541	9532	9524	9515	9506	9497	9489	9480	9471	.05
.06	9462	9454	9445	9436	9428	9419	9410	9402	9393	9384	.06
.07	9376	9367	9358	9350	9341	9333	9324	9315	9307	9298	.07
.08	9290	9281	9273	9264	9256	9247	9238	9230	9221	9213	.08
.09	9204	9196	9188	9179	9171	9162	9154	9145	9137	9129	.09
.10	9120	9112	9103	9095	9087	9078	9070	9061	9053	9045	.10
.11	9036	9028	9020	9012	9003	8995	8987	8978	8970	8962	.11
.12	8954	8945	8937	8929	8921	8913	8904	8896	8888	8880	.12
.13	8872	8863	8855	8847	8839	8831	8823	8815	8806	8798	.13
.14	8790	8782	8774	8766	8758	8750	8742	8734	8726	8718	.14
.15	8710	8702	8694	8686	8678	8670	8662	8654	8646	8638	.15
.16	8630	8622	8614	8606	8598	8590	8582	8574	8566	8559	.16
.17	8551	8543	8535	8527	8519	8511	8504	8496	8488	8480	.17
.18	8472	8464	8457	8449	8441	8433	8426	.8418	8410	8402	.18
.19	8395	8387	8379	8371	8364	8356	8348	8341	8333	8325	.19

Δm	0	1	2	3	4	5	6	7	8	9	Δm
0.20	8318	8310	8302	8295	8287	8279	8272	8264	8257	8249	0.20
.21	8241	8234	8226	8219	8211	8204	8196	8188	8181	8173	.21
.22	8166	8158	8151	8143	8136	8128	8121	8113	8106	8098	.22
.23	8091	8084	8076	8069	8061	8054	8046	8039	8032	8024	.23
.24	8017	8009	8002	7995	7987	7980	7973	7965	7958	7951	.24
.25	7943	7936	7929	7921	7914	7907	7900	7892	7885	7878	.25
.26	7870	7863	7856	7849	7842	7834	7827	7820	7813	7805	.26
.27	7798	7791	7784	7777	7770	7762	7755	7748	7741	7734	.27
.28	7727	7720	7713	7705	7698	7691	7684	7677	7670	7663	.28
.29	7656	7649	7642	7635	7628	7621	7614	7607	7600	7593	.29
.30	7586	7579	7572	7565	7558	7551	7544	7537	7530	7523	.30
.31	7516	7509	7502	7495	7489	7482	7475	7468	7461	7454	.31
.32	7447	7440	7434	7427	7420	7413	7406	7399	7393	7386	.32
.33	7379	7372	7365	7359	7352	7345	7338	7332	7325	7318	.33
.34	7311	7305	7298	7291	7285	7278	7271	7264	7258	7251	.34
.35	7244	7238	7231	7224	7218	7211	7204	7198	7191	7185	.35
.36	7178	7171	7165	7158	7152	7145	7138	7132	7125	7119	.36
.37	7112	7106	7099	7093	7086	7079	7073	7066	7060	7053	.37
.38	7047	7040	7034	7027	7021	7015	7008	7002	6995	6989	.38
.39	6982	6976	6969	6963	6957	6950	6944	6937	6931	6925	.39
.40	6918	6912	6906	6899	6893	6887	6880	6874	6868	6861	.40
.41	6855	6849	6842	6836	6830	6823	6817	6811	6805	6798	.41
.42	6792	6786	6780	6773	6767	6761	6755	6748	6742	6736	.42
.43	6730	6724	6717	6711	6705	6699	6693	6687	6680	6674	.43
.44	6668	6662	6656	6650	6644	6637	6631	6625	6619	6613	.44
.45	6607	6601	6595	6589	6583	6577	6571	6564	6558	6552	.45
.46	6546	6540	6534	6528	6522	6516	6510	6504	6498	6492	.46
.47	6486	6480	6474	6468	6462	6457	6451	6445	6439	6433	.47
.48	6427	6421	6415	6409	6403	6397	6391	6386	6380	6374	.48
.49	6368	6362	6356	6350	6345	6339	6333	6327	6321	6315	.49
.50	.6310	.6304	.6298	.6292	.6286	.6281	.6275	.6269	.6263	.6257	.50
.51	6252	6246	6240	6234	6229	6223	6217	6212	6206	6200	.51
.52	6194	6189	6183	6177	6172	6166	6160	6155	6149	6143	.52
.53	6138	6132	6126	6121	6115	6109	6104	6098	6093	6087	.53
.54	6081	6076	6070	6065	6059	6053	6048	6042	6037	6031	.54
.55	6026	6020	6015	6009	6003	5998	5992	5987	5981	5976	.55
.56	5970	5965	5959	5954	5948	5943	5937	5932	5927	5921	.56
.57	5916	5910	5905	5899	5894	5888	5883	5878	5872	5867	.57
.58	5861	5856	5851	5845	5840	5834	5829	5824	5818	5813	.58
.59	5808	5802	5797	5792	5786	5781	5776	5770	5765	5760	.59

Δm	0	1	2	3	4	5	6	7	8	9	Δm
0.60	5754	5749	5744	5739	5733	5728	5723	5717	5712	5707	0.60
.61	5702	5696	5691	5686	5681	5675	5670	5665	5660	5655	.61
.62	5649	5644	5639	5634	5629	5623	5618	5613	5608	5603	.62
.63	5598	5592	5587	5582	5577	5572	5567	5562	5556	5551	.63
.64	5546	5541	5536	5531	5526	5521	5516	5511	5506	5500	.64
.65	5495	5490	5485	5480	5475	5470	5465	5460	5455	5450	.65
.66	5445	5440	5435	5430	5425	5420	5415	5410	5405	5400	.66
.67	5395	5390	5385	5380	5375	5370	5365	5360	5355	5351	.67
.68	5346	5341	5336	5331	5326	5321	5316	5311	5306	5302	.68
.69	5297	5292	5287	5282	5277	5272	5267	5263	5258	5253	.69
.70	5248	5243	5238	5234	5229	5224	5219	5214	5210	5205	.70
.71	5200	5195	5190	5186	5181	5176	5171	5167	5162	5157	.71
.72	5152	5148	5143	5138	5133	5129	5124	5119	5114	5110	.72
.73	5105	5100	5096	5091	5086	5082	5077	5072	5068	5063	.73
.74	5058	5054	5049	5044	5040	5035	5030	5026	5021	5016	.74
.75	5012	5007	5003	4998	4993	4989	4984	4980	4975	4970	.75
.76	4966	4961	4957	4952	4948	4943	4939	4934	4929	4925	.76
.77	4920	4916	4911	4907	4902	4898	4893	4889	4884	4880	.77
.78	4875	4871	4866	4862	4857	4853	4848	4844	4839	4835	.78
.79	4831	4826	4822	4817	4813	4808	4804	4800	4795	4791	.79
.80	4786	4782	4777	4773	4769	4764	4760	4756	4751	4747	.80
.81	4742	4738	4734	4729	4725	4721	4716	4712	4708	4703	.81
.82	4699	4695	4690	4686	4682	4677	4673	4669	4664	4660	.82
.83	4656	4652	4647	4643	4639	4634	4630	4626	4622	4617	.83
.84	4613	4609	4605	4600	4596	4592	4588	4584	4579	4575	.84
.85	4571	4567	4562	4558	4554	4550	4546	4542	4537	4533	.85
.86	4529	4525	4521	4516	4512	4508	4504	4500	4496	4492	.86
.87	4487	4483	4479	4475	4471	4467	4463	4459	4455	4450	.87
.88	4446	4442	4438	4434	4430	4426	4422	4418	4414	4410	.83
.89	4406	4401	4397	4393	4389	4385	4381	4377	4373	4369	.89
.90	4365	4361	4357	4353	4349	4345	4341	4337	4333	4329	.90
.91	4325	4321	4317	4313	4309	4305	4301	4297	4293	4289	.91
.92	4285	4282	4278	4274	4270	4266	4262	4258	4254	4250	.92
.93	4246	4242	4238	4234	4231	4227	4223	4219	4215	4211	.93
.94	4207	4203	4200	4196	4192	4188	4184	4180	4176	4173	.94
.95	4169	4165	4161	4157	4153	4150	4146	4142	4138	4134	.95
.96	4130	4127	4123	4119	4115	4111	4108	4104	4100	4096	.96
.97	4093	4089	4085	4081	4078	4074	4070	4066	4063	4059	.97
.98	4055	4051	4048	4044	4040	4036	4033	4029	4025	4022	.98
0.99	4018	4014	4011	4007	4003	3999	3996	3992	3988	3985	0.99
1.00	3981	3977	3974	3970	3966	3963	3959	3955	3952	3948	1.00

Δm	0	1	2	3	4	5	6	7	8	9	Δm
1.00	.3981	.3977	.3974	.3970	.3966	.3963	.3959	.3955	.3952	.3948	1.00
.01	3945	3941	3937	3934	3930	3926	3923	3919	3916	3912	.01
.02	3908	3905	3901	3898	3894	3890	3887	3883	3880	3876	.02
.03	3873	3869	3865	3862	3858	3855	3851	3848	3844	3841	.03
.04	3837	3834	3830	3826	3823	3819	3816	3812	3809	3805	.04
.05	3802	3798	3795	3791	3788	3784	3781	3777	3774	3771	.05
.06	3767	3764	3760	3757	3753	3750	3746	3743	3739	3736	.06
.07	3733	3729	3726	3722	3719	3715	3712	3709	3705	3702	.07
.08	3698	3695	3691	3688	3685	3681	3678	3675	3671	3668	.08
.09	3664	3661	3658	3654	3651	3648	3644	3641	3637	3634	.09
.10	3631	3627	3624	3621	3617	3614	3611	3607	3604	3601	.10
.11	3597	3594	3591	3588	3584	3581	3578	3574	3571	3568	.11
.12	3565	3561	3558	3555	3551	3548	3545	3542	3538	3535	.12
.13	3532	3529	3525	3522	3519	3516	3512	3509	3506	3503	.13
.14	3499	3496	3493	3490	3487	3483	3480	3477	3474	3471	.14
.15	3467	3464	3461	3458	3455	3451	3448	3445	3442	3439	.15
.16	3436	3432	3429	3426	3423	3420	3417	3414	3410	3407	.16
.17	3404	3401	3398	3395	3392	3388	3385	3382	3379	3376	.17
.18	3373	3370	3367	3364	3360	3357	3354	3351	3348	3345	.18
.19	3342	3339	3336	3333	3330	3327	3324	3320	3317	3314	.19
.20	3311	3308	3305	3302	3299	3296	3293	3290	3287	3284	.20
.21	3281	3278	3275	3272	3269	3266	3263	3260	3257	3254	.21
.22	3251	3248	3245	3242	3239	3236	3233	3230	3227	3224	.22
.23	3221	3218	3215	3212	3209	3206	3203	3200	3197	3194	.23
.24	3192	3189	3186	3183	3180	3177	3174	3171	3168	3165	.24
.25	3162	3159	3156	3154	3151	3148	3145	3142	3139	3136	.25
.26	3133	.3130	3128	3125	3122	3119	3116	3113	3110	3107	.26
.27	3105	3102	3099	3096	3093	3090	3087	3085	3082	3079	.27
.28	3076	3073	3070	3068	3065	3062	3059	3056	3054	3051	.28
.29	3048	3045	3042	3039	3037	3034	3031	3028	3026	3023	.29
.30	3020	3017	3014	3012	3009	3006	3003	3001	2998	2995	.30
.31	2993	2990	2987	2984	2981	2979	2976	2973	2970	2968	.31
.32	2965	2962	2959	2957	2954	2951	2948	2946	2943	2940	.32
.33	2938	2935	2932	2930	2927	2924	2921	2919	2916	2913	.33
.34	2911	2908	2905	2903	2900	2897	2895	2892	2889	2887	.34
.35	2884	2881	2879	2876	2873	2871	2868	2865	2863	2860	.35
.36	2858	2855	2852	2850	2847	2844	2842	2839	2837	2834	.36
.37	2831	2829	2826	2824	2821	2818	2816	2813	2811	2808	.37
.38	2805	2803	2800	2798	2795	2793	2790	2787	2785	2782	.38
.39	2780	2777	2775	2772	2769	2767	2764	2762	2759	2757	.39

Δm	0	1	2	3	4	5	6	7	8	9	Δm
1.40	2754	2752	2749	2747	2744	2742	2739	2737	2734	2731	1.40
.41	2729	2726	2724	2721	2719	2716	2714	2711	2709	2706	.41
.42	2704	2701	2699	2696	2694	2692	2689	2687	2684	2682	.42
.43	2679	2677	2674	2672	2669	2667	2664	2662	2660	2657	.43
.44	2655	2652	2650	2647	2645	2642	2640	2638	2635	2633	.44
.45	2630	2628	2625	2623	2621	2618	2616	2613	2611	2609	.45
.46	2606	2604	2601	2599	2597	2594	2592	2589	2587	2585	.46
.47	2582	2580	2578	2575	2573	2570	2568	2566	2563	2561	.47
.48	2559	2556	2554	2552	2549	2547	2544	2542	2540	2537	.48
.49	2535	2533	2530	2528	2526	2523	2521	2519	2517	2514	.49
.50	.2512	.2510	.2507	.2505	.2503	.2500	.2498	.2496	.2493	.2491	.50
.51	2489	2487	2484	2482	2480	2477	2475	2473	2471	2468	.51
.52	2466	2464	2462	2459	2457	2455	2452	2450	2448	2445	.52
.53	2443	2441	2439	2437	2434	2432	2430	2428	2425	2423	.53
.54	2421	2419	2417	2414	2412	2410	2408	2405	2403	2401	.54
.55	2399	2397	2394	2392	2390	2388	2386	2383	2381	2379	.55
.56	2377	2375	2372	2370	2368	2366	2364	2362	2359	2357	.56
.57	2355	2353	2351	2349	2346	2344	2342	2340	2338	2336	.57
.58	2333	2331	2329	2327	2325	2323	2321	2318	2316	2314	.58
.59	2312	2310	2308	2306	2304	2301	2299	2297	2295	2293	.59
.60	2291	2289	2287	2285	2282	2280	2278	2276	2274	2272	.60
.61	2270	2268	2266	2264	2262	2259	2257	2255	2253	2251	.61
.62	2249	2247	2245	2243	2241	2239	2237	2235	2233	2230	.62
.63	2228	2226	2224	2222	2220	2218	2216	2214	2212	2210	.63
.64	2208	2206	2204	2202	2200	2198	2196	2194	2192	2190	.64
.65	2188	2186	2184	2182	2180	2178	2176	2174	2172	2170	.65
.66	2168	2166	2164	2162	2160	2158	2156	2154	2152	2150	.66
.67	2148	2146	2144	2142	2140	2138	2136	2134	2132	2130	.67
.68	2128	2126	2124	2122	2120	2118	2116	2114	2113	2111	.68
.69	2109	2107	2105	2103	2101	2099	2097	2095	2093	2091	.69
.70	2089	2087	2085	2084	2082	2080	2078	2076	2074	2072	.70
.71	2070	2068	2066	2064	2063	2061	2059	2057	2055	2053	.71
.72	2051	2049	2047	2046	2044	2042	2040	2038	2036	2034	.72
.73	2032	2030	2029	2027	2025	2023	2021	2019	2017	2016	.73
.74	2014	2012	2010	2008	2006	2004	2003	2001	1999	1997	.74
.75	1995	1993	1992	1990	1988	1986	1984	1982	1981	1979	.75
.76	1977	1975	1973	1972	1970	1968	1966	1964	1962	1961	.76
.77	1959	1957	1955	1953	1952	1950	1948	1946	1944	1943	.77
.78	1941	1939	1937	1936	1934	1932	1930	1928	1927	1925	.78
.79	1923	1921	1920	1918	1916	1914	1912	1911	1909	1907	.79

Δm	0	1	2	3	4	5	6	7	8	9	Δm
1.80	1905	1904	1902	1900	1898	1897	1895	1893	1891	1890	1.80
.81	1888	1886	1885	1883	1881	1879	1878	1876	1874	1872	.81
.82	1871	1869	1867	1866	1864	1862	1860	1859	1857	1855	.82
.83	1854	1852	1850	1848	1847	1845	1843	1842	1840	1838	.83
.84	1837	1835	1833	1831	1830	1828	1826	1825	1823	1821	.84
.85	1820	1818	1816	1815	1813	1811	1810	1808	1806	1805	.85
.86	1803	1801	1800	1798	1796	1795	1793	1791	1790	1788	.86
.87	1786	1785	1783	1782	1780	1778	1777	1775	1773	1772	.87
.88	1770	1768	1767	1765	1764	1762	1760	1759	1757	1755	.88
.89	1754	1752	1751	1749	1747	1746	1744	1743	1741	1739	.89
.90	1738	1736	1735	1733	1731	1730	1728	1727	1725	1723	.90
.91	1722	1720	1719	1717	1716	1714	1712	1711	1709	1708	.91
.92	1706	1705	1703	1701	1700	1698	1697	1695	1694	1692	.92
.93	1690	1689	1687	1686	1684	1683	1681	1680	1678	1676	.93
.94	1675	1673	1672	1670	1669	1667	1666	1664	1663	1661	.94
.95	1660	1658	1657	1655	1653	1652	1650	1649	1647	1646	.95
.96	1644	1643	1641	1640	1638	1637	1635	1634	1632	1631	.96
.97	1629	1628	1626	1625	1623	1622	1620	1619	1617	1616	.97
.98	1614	1613	1611	1610	1608	1607	1605	1604	1603	1601	.98
1.99	1600	1598	1597	1595	1594	1592	1591	1589	1588	1586	1.99
2.00	1585	1583	1582	1581	1579	1578	1576	1575	1573	1572	2.00